Bitesize
AQA GCSE (9–1)
MATHEMATICS

REVISION WORKBOOK

HIGHER

eries Consultant:
arry Smith

uthor:
avtej Marwaha

Contents

☑ Tick off each topic as you go.

Fractions, decimals and percentages

⑤ Quick quiz

1. Circle the fraction that converts to a terminating decimal.

IS NOT RECURRING

$\frac{1}{9}$ (⃝$\frac{1}{10}$) ✓ $\frac{1}{11}$ $\frac{1}{12}$

2. Work out these calculations.

(a) 45% of 70   **(b)** 32% of 180   **(c)** $\frac{4}{5}$ of 90   **(d)** $\frac{5}{8}$ of 160

31.5 ✓   57.6 ✓   72 ✓   100 ✓

⑩ Working from a whole   Grade 4

1. There are 300 counters in a bag. Each counter is black, white or grey. 30% of the counters are black and $\frac{1}{4}$ of the counters are white.

Work out the number of grey counters in the bag.   **[3 marks]**

> Convert the fraction into a percentage.

> The whole is 100%.

$30\% + \frac{1}{4} = 30\% + \underline{25}\% = \underline{55}\%$

$100\% - \underline{55}\% = \underline{45}\%$

Exam focus
Always write out the percentage as a fraction to make the process clear.

$\underline{45}\%$ of $300 = \dfrac{45}{100} \times 300 = \underline{135}$

2. All the pupils in Year 11 were asked to choose which sport they preferred out of football, rugby, hockey, tennis or badminton. The table shows the results, as proportions.

Football	Rugby	Hockey	Tennis	Badminton
24%	0.16	$\frac{1}{4}$	20%	

(a) What percentage of the pupils prefer:
(i) rugby or hockey   **[1 mark]**   **(ii)** badminton?   **[1 mark]**

41 ✓ %   15. ✓ %

There are 150 pupils in Year 11.
(b) How many chose football?   **[2 marks]**

36 ✓

⑤ Recurring decimals   Grade 8

. Show that $0.1\dot{7}\dot{8}$ can be written as the fraction $\dfrac{59}{330}$.   **[3 marks]**

ASK MRS LYNAM!

$x = 0.1\dot{7}\dot{8}$

$1000x = 178.7\dot{8}$

$-10x = 0.78$

$990x = 178$ (178?)

$\dfrac{178}{990}$ $\dfrac{59}{330}$

$x = \dfrac{177}{990} = \dfrac{59}{330}$

Manipulating fractions

Match the operations to the methods.

Adding or subtracting fractions	Multiply the numerators and multiply the denominators
Multiplying fractions ~~WORKING~~	Invert the second fraction then multiply
Dividing fractions KFC!	Find equivalent fractions with the same denominator

⑮ **The four operations** **Grades 4–5** ☑

1. Work out the answers to these calculations. Give your answers in their simplest form.

(a) $\frac{13}{7} \times \frac{5}{6_2}$ **[2 marks]**

$= \frac{1 \times 5}{7 \times 2}$

When multiplying fractions, check to see if you can cancel first.

$\frac{5}{14}$

(b) $\frac{3}{10} \div \frac{11}{20}$ **[2 marks]**

$= \frac{3}{10} \times \frac{20}{11}$

$= \frac{3 \times 20}{10 \times 11}$

$\frac{6}{11}$

(c) $3\frac{1}{2} - 1\frac{3}{5}$ **[3 marks]**

$= \frac{(3 \times 2) + 1}{2} - \frac{(5 \times 1) + 3}{5}$

$= \frac{7}{2} - \frac{8}{5} = \frac{35}{10} - \frac{16}{10}$

$\frac{19}{10} = 1\frac{9}{10}$

Exam focus
Make sure you clearly show your working out when dealing with fractions.

Always convert mixed numbers to improper fractions first.

2. Work out the answers to these calculations, giving your answers in their simplest form.

(a) $3\frac{3}{8} + 4\frac{2}{5}$ **[3 marks]**

$7\frac{31}{40}$

(b) $4\frac{4}{7} - 2\frac{2}{3}$ **[3 marks]**

$1\frac{19}{21}$

(c) $1\frac{1}{3} \times \frac{7}{10} \div \frac{2}{5}$ **[3 marks]**

$2\frac{1}{3}$

⑩ **Working with fractions in context** **Grade 5** ☑

3. 120 children compete in a charity race. $\frac{1}{4}$ of the children don't complete the race.
Work out the number of children who complete the race. **[3 marks]**

90

4. A headteacher collected information about 225 Year 11 students.
$\frac{1}{3}$ of the students wanted to go to college and $\frac{2}{5}$ of the students wanted to do apprenticeships.
The rest of the students wanted to stay on at school.
Work out the number of students who wanted to stay on at school. **[3 marks]**

60

5. Mischa is cutting a cake. She gives $\frac{1}{3}$ of the cake to Tom and gives $\frac{1}{4}$ of the cake to Olivia.
Mischa keeps the rest of the cake. Olivia only wants half her slice and gives the rest of it back to Mischa.
What fraction of the whole cake does Mischa now have in total? **[4 marks]**

$\frac{13}{24}$

☑ **Made a start** ☑ **Feeling confident** ☑ **Exam ready**

Percentage change

---

2 Quick quiz

1. 'Per cent' means out of .... **100** .... **3.** 25% of 80 = ... **20** ....

2. 10% of 60 = ... **6** .... **4.** 50% of 90 = ... **45** ....

---

10 Percentage change **Grade 4**

1. Work out the percentage increase or decrease.

> To find the percentage increase or decrease, find the difference, divide it by the original amount and multiply by 100.

(a) 36.4 g to 41.3 g **[2 marks]**

$41.3 - 36.4 = 4.9$

$\frac{4.9}{36.4} \times 100 = $ .... **13.45** ....%

(b) 83.4 m to 69.5 m **[2 marks]**

.... **16.7** ....%

(c) 16.38 kg to 24.56 kg **[2 marks]**

$24.56 - 16.38$ 49.9

$\frac{8.18}{16.38} \times 100 = $ .... 49.9 ~~49.18~~ ....%

2. (a) Increase 840 by 28%. **[2 marks]**

$\frac{28}{100} \times 840 = $ **235.2**

$840 + $ **235.2** $= $ 1075.2   .... **1075.2** ....

(b) Decrease 238 by 18%. **[2 marks]**

$238 \times 0.82 = $ **195.16**

.... **195.2** ....

(c) Increase £63.50 by 45%. **[2 marks]**

£ **92.07**

> To increase or decrease an amount by a percentage, find the percentage of the original amount, then add or subtract it to or from the original amount. Alternatively, use the multiplier method.

---

10 Everyday percentages **Grade 4**

3. Gary buys and sells antique clocks. He wants to reach a target of at least 30% profit on each antique clock he sells. In January, Gary buys an antique clock for £2500. In February, Gary sells the antique clock for £3250. Does Gary reach his target for this antique clock? **[3 marks]**

30% of £2500 = 750

2500 + 750 = £3250

.... Yes 30% increase ....

4. The table shows the costs, per person, of a holiday at two different hotels. It shows the cost for 5 nights per adult and the cost for each extra night. It also shows the discount for each child, which is applied to the adult price.

	Hotel 1		Hotel 2	
	Cost for 5 nights	**Cost for each extra night**	**Cost for 5 nights**	**Cost for each extra night**
1 Apr – 31 May	£1269	£160	£949	£95
1 Jun – 16 Jul	£1329	£160	£1319	£105
17 Jul – 31 Aug	£1720	£170	£1950	£300
Discount for each child	10% off		25% off	

There are 2 adults and 2 children in the Arya family. The family want a holiday for 7 nights, starting on 1 August. One hotel will be cheaper than the other hotel for them. Work out which hotel offers the cheaper stay. You must show your working. **[5 marks]**

.... Hotel ~~2~~ 1 ....

 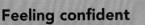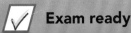

Reverse percentages

Match the multipliers to the correct percentage change.

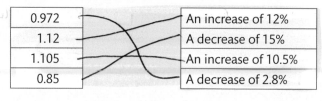

0.972	An increase of 12%
1.12	A decrease of 15%
1.105	An increase of 10.5%
0.85	A decrease of 2.8%

 Working out the normal price   **Grade 5**

1. The normal price of a television is reduced by 35% in a sale.
The sale price of the television is £780.
Work out the normal price of the television.

> The normal price is always 100%.

[3 marks]

Method 1

> Subtract the percentage reduction from 100% and equate this value with the sale price.

Sale price = 100% − 35%

$= \underline{\quad 65 \quad}$ %

£780 = $\underline{\quad 65 \quad}$ %

$1\% = \dfrac{780}{65}$

$100\% = \dfrac{780}{65} \times 100$

£ ___1200___

Method 2

> To find the multiplier, subtract from 100% and then divide by 100 to convert into a decimal.

100% − 35% = $\underline{\quad 65 \quad}$ %

$\underline{6.5} \div 100 = \underline{0.65}$

Normal price = £780 ÷ $\underline{0.65}$

£ ___1200___

Exam focus 📌

Choose the method that you find easiest.

2. In a sale, normal prices are reduced by 12.5%.
The normal price of a tablet is reduced by £18.
Work out the normal price of the tablet.   **[3 marks]**

> Work out the multiplier: 100% − 12.5%, then convert into a decimal.

100 − 12.5 = 87.5

87.5 ÷ 100 = 0.875

18 ÷ 0.875 = £ ___20.57___

$18 \div 12.5\%$

$\dfrac{18}{0.125} = £144$

3. Each year, Sol records how long it takes him, on average, to get to work each day. In 2017, he took 8% more time than in 2016. In 2017, the average time he took to get to work was 34 minutes. Work out the average time he took to get to work in 2016.
Give your answer to the nearest minute.   **[3 marks]**

$108\% = 34$

$8 \div 100 = 800.08$

$34 \div 0.08 =$

31   34 ÷ 425 ___ minutes

4. Ravina has two investments: a fixed bond and an ISA. During a 5-year period, the value of the fixed bond increased by 5% to £40 530. In the same period, the value of the ISA increased by 7.5% to £27 004.
In this 5-year period, which investment has grown more in terms of monetary value?   **[4 marks]**

fixed bond = £1930

ISA = £1884

fixed bond grew mor

 Made a start   **Feeling confident**   **Exam ready**

Growth and decay

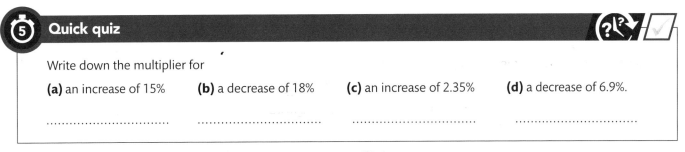

⑤ Quick quiz

Write down the multiplier for

(a) an increase of 15%　　　**(b)** a decrease of 18%　　　**(c)** an increase of 2.35%　　　**(d)** a decrease of 6.9%.

....　　...........................　　...........................　　...........................

⑤ Growth　　　Grade 5

1. Alan invests £1800 at 2.75% per annum compound interest.
   Work out the value of Alan's investment after 3 years.　　**[3 marks]**

   | As it is an increase, add the percentage. |

   ⛳ 100% + ...% = ...%

   　　Multiplier = ...% ÷ 100 = ...

   　　Value of investment = 1800 × (...............)³

   　　　　　　£......................

   Exam focus
   Make sure you give your answer to 2 decimal places. 📌

⑤ Decay　　　Grade 5

2. John buys a new car for £32 400. The value of the car depreciates at the rate of 15% per year. After *n* years, the value of the car is £19 897.65.
   Work out the value of *n*.　　**[2 marks]**

   | As it is a decrease, subtract the percentage. |

   ⛳ 100% − ....% = ...%

   　　Multiplier = ...% ÷ 100 = ...

   　　Value = 32 400 × (...............)^n = £19 897.65

   | Try different values of *n*. |

   　　　　　$n = $......................

⑩ Money　　　Grade 5

3. Bruna invests £6000 in a savings account for 3 years. The account pays compound interest at an annual rate of 5% for the first year, 4% for the second year and *x*% for the third year.
   There is a total amount of £6715.80 in the savings account at the end of 3 years.
   Work out the rate of interest in the third year.

   | Set up an equation. Write the multiplier for an increase by *x*% as $1 + \dfrac{x}{100}$. |

   　　　　　　　　　　　　　　[4 marks]

   .... %

4. Claude buys some shares for £1800 at the beginning of 2012. The value of the shares increases by 8% each year.
   Work out the value of the shares at the beginning of 2018.　　**[2 marks]**

   £...............................

⑤ Populations　　　Grade 5

5. A scientist studies a rabbit population. She finds that the population has been decreasing due to disease. The scientist assumes that it is decreasing at a rate of 12% each year. At the beginning of 2012, the rabbit population was 4800. Using the scientist's assumption, work out the size of this rabbit population at the start of 2017.　　**[2 marks]**

   ....

Estimation and counting

② Quick quiz

Round each number to 1 significant figure.

(a) 82.6 ......80...... ✓   **(b)** 195.5 ......200...... ✓   **(c)** 0.198 ......0.2...... ✓   **(d)** 0.523 ......0.5...... ✓

⑤ Counting   Grade 5

1. There are 18 men and 25 women at a dancing club. One of the men and one of the women will pair up to perform the first dance.

  (a) Work out the number of different pairs that can be chosen.   **[2 marks]**

  ....

  Two women are to be chosen to perform the second dance.

  Ashley thinks the number of different pairs that can be chosen is 600. Lisa thinks the number of different pairs that can be chosen is 300.

  (b) Who is correct, Ashley or Lisa? Tick a box.   **[2 marks]**

    Ashley ☐   Lisa ☐

  Give a reason for your answer.

....

2. There are 18 girls and 15 boys in a club. One girl and one boy are going to be chosen to go to a conference. Work out the total number of ways of choosing a girl and a boy.   **[2 marks]**

  ....

⑮ Estimating an answer   Grades 5–6

3. Estimate

  (a) $\dfrac{204 \times 9.95}{0.509}$ **[2 marks]**

    $= \dfrac{200 \times \text{.......}}{0.5} = \dfrac{\square}{0.5}$

  ....

  (b) $\sqrt{4.99 \times 2.05 + 7.24}$ **[3 marks]**

    $= \sqrt{5 \times \text{..................}}$

  ....

4. The radius of a circle is 5.4 cm.

  (a) Estimate the area of the circle.   **[2 marks]**

  .... cm²

  (b) Without further calculation, comment on whether your method gives you an overestimate or an underestimate for the area of the circle.   **[1 mark]**

....

5. Kathy has some cows. The cows produce an average total of 22.3 litres of milk per day for 191 days. Kathy sells the milk in half-litre cartons. Estimate the total number of cartons that Kathy will be able to fill with the milk produced over the 191 days. You **must** show your working.   **[3 marks]**

  ....

> **Exam focus** 📌
> Write each number correct to 1 significant figure. Make it clear how you have rounded each individual number.

> Remember BIDMAS.

> The numerical value of π is approximately 3.14.

> The area of a circle is πr^2.

> When estimating, always round to 1 significant figure.

Upper and lower bounds

Choose the correct word in each sentence by circling it.

(a) To find the upper bound, you (**add**) / **subtract** half of the unit to which you are rounding.

(b) To find the lower bound you **add** / (**subtract**) half of the unit to which you are rounding.

---

⑩ **Working out upper and lower bounds** — Grade 8

1. Each of these values has been rounded to 1 significant figure. Write down the upper and lower bound for each value.

(a) 2000 m **[1 mark]**

LB: ......1500...... m

UB: ......2500...... m

(b) 0.6 kg **[1 mark]**

LB: ......0.55...... kg

UB: ......0.~~7~~65...... kg

(c) 5 seconds **[1 mark]**

LB: ......4.5...... s

UB: ......~~6~~5.5...... s

(d) 10 miles **[1 mark]**

LB: ......9.5...... miles

UB: ......10.5...... miles

2. $T = \dfrac{x}{y + z}$ where $x = 98.3$ correct to 1 decimal place, $y = 21$ correct to 2 significant figures and $z = 15.23$ correct to 2 decimal places.

Work out the upper bound for the value of T. Give your answer to 1 decimal place. You **must** show your working. **[4 marks]**

For the upper bound of T, the numerator will be an upper bound and the denominator will be a lower bound.

The lower bound of the denominator must be the sum of the lower bounds of the two numbers.

Set up a table of upper and lower bounds for each value.

	x	y	z
UB	98.35	21.5	15.235
LB	98.25	20.5	15.225

$T = \dfrac{x}{y + z} = \dfrac{98.35}{20.5 + 15.225} = 35.725$ = ...2.8...... ✓

---

⑩ **Using upper and lower bounds** — Grade 8

3. Mark runs 200 metres, correct to the nearest metre. He takes 25.3 seconds, correct to the nearest 0.1 of a second. Work out the lower bound of Mark's average speed. Give your answer to 3 significant figures. **[3 marks]**

If the distance has been rounded to the nearest metre, the actual value could be ±0.5 m.

.... m/s

4. A soda machine makes fizzy drinks. The machine puts 220 ml fizzy water (measured correct to the nearest ml) and 29 ml cordial (measured correct to the nearest ml) into each bottle.
The volume of a bottle is 250 ml, correct to the nearest 0.1 ml.
Tom thinks the total volume of the drink could be greater than the capacity of the bottle. Is he correct?
Give a reason for your answer. **[3 marks]**

First work out the bounds for each liquid and then find the lower bound of the capacity.

....

BBC

Accuracy and error

② Quick quiz

1. A rope is 24.3 m long, correct to 1 decimal place. Write down the

   (a) upper bound   .... m

   (b) lower bound.   .... m

2. A wall is 18 m long, correct to 2 significant figures. Write down the error interval for the length, *l* cm, of the wall.

   .... $\leq l <$ ....

⑳ Giving answers to an appropriate degree of accuracy   Grade 8

1. The length of the side of a metal cube is 113 mm correct to the nearest mm. The mass of the cube is 3.48 kg correct to 2 decimal places. Work out the value of the density of the metal to an appropriate degree of accuracy. Give your answer in g/cm³. You must explain why your answer is to an appropriate degree of accuracy. **[5 marks]**

	Mass	Length
UB	3.485 kg	
LB		112.5 mm

Set up a table of upper and lower bound values.

Convert kilograms to grams and millimetres to centimetres.

To find the upper bound of density, you must find the upper bound of mass and the lower bound of volume.

$$\text{Upper bound} = \frac{\text{mass}}{\text{volume}}$$

$$= \frac{\ldots\ldots \times 1000}{(\ldots\ldots \div 10)^3} \text{ g/cm}^3$$

$$= \ldots\ldots \text{ g/cm}^3$$

$$\text{Lower bound} = \frac{\text{mass}}{\text{volume}}$$

$$= \frac{\ldots\ldots \times 1000}{(\ldots\ldots \div 10)^3} \text{ g/cm}^3$$

$$= \ldots\ldots \text{ g/cm}^3$$

Density = ... g/cm³ to .... decimal place(s)

This is the appropriate degree of accuracy because both values round to the same number when rounded to .... decimal place(s).

2. $P = \dfrac{E}{10b}$, $E = 68.65$ correct to 2 decimal places and $b = 2.243$ correct to 3 decimal places.

By considering bounds, work out the value of *P* to a suitable degree of accuracy. You **must** show your working. Give a reason for your answer. **[5 marks]**

Work out the upper and lower bounds for *E* and *b* and use these to find the upper and lower bounds for *P*.

....

....

3. Hannah drops a ball from a height of *h* metres onto the ground.

The time, *t* seconds, that the ball takes to reach the ground is given by $t = \sqrt{\dfrac{2h}{g}}$, where *g* m/s² is the acceleration due to gravity, $h = 84.9$ correct to 1 decimal place and $g = 9.8$ correct to 2 significant figures. By considering bounds, work out the value of *t* to a suitable degree of accuracy. You **must** show your working. Give a reason for your answer. **[5 marks]**

....

....

   ✓ **Made a start**   ✓ **Feeling confident**   ✓ **Exam ready**

3.14

Factors and primes

Quick quiz

Write in the missing powers.

(a) $2 \times 2 \times 2 \times 3 \times 3 \times 5 = 2^{\square} \times 3^{\square} \times 5$

(b) $5 \times 5 \times 7 \times 11 \times 11 \times 11 = 5^{\square} \times 7 \times 11^{\square}$

 Product of prime factors | **Grade 5**

1. What is 72 as a product of its prime factors?
Circle your answer.

$2 \times 3^3 \qquad 2^2 \times 3^3 \qquad 2^3 \times 3^2 \qquad 2^3 \times 3$ **[1 mark]**

2. Write 180 as a product of its prime factors. **[2 marks]**

....

 Working out highest common factors and lowest common multiples  **Grade 5**

3. (a) Write 75 as a product of powers of its prime factors. **[2 marks]**

Use a factor tree to write 75 as a product of its prime numbers.

$75 = 3 \times \text{............} \times \text{............}$

....

(b) Work out the highest common factor of 75 and 90. **[2 marks]**

$75 = ③ \times ⑤ \times 5$
$90 = 2 \times ③ \times 3 \times ⑤$

Circle the numbers that appear in **both** lists.

$HCF = 3 \times \text{............................}$

....

(c) Work out the lowest common multiple of 75 and 90. **[1 mark]**

$75 = 3 \times 5 \times 5$
$90 = 2 \times 3 \times 3 \times 5$

Look for the numbers that appear in **either** list.

$LCM = 2 \times 3 \times \text{............} \times 5 \times \text{............}$

....

4. $X = 2^2 \times 3 \times 5^2$ and $Y = 2^3 \times 5$.

(a) Work out the highest common factor (HCF) of X and Y. **[1 mark]**

....

(b) Work out the lowest common multiple (LCM) of X and Y. **[2 marks]**

....

5. The highest common factor (HCF) of two numbers is 9. The lowest common multiple (LCM) of two numbers is a multiple of 15.
Write down **two** possible numbers that satisfy these conditions. **[2 marks]**

....

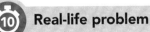 **Real-life problem**  **Grade 5**

6. Asha is planning a party. She wants to buy some naans and some kebabs. She is expecting more than 75 guests. A pack of 6 naans costs £1.75. A pack of 9 kebabs costs £3.40. Asha wants to buy more than 75 naans and more than 75 kebabs. She wants to buy exactly the same number of naans as kebabs. Work out the smallest amount of money that Asha could spend. **[5 marks]**

£ ....

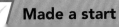 **Made a start** 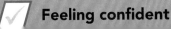 **Feeling confident** **Exam ready**

Standard form

② Quick quiz

1. Write each number as a power of 10.

(a) 1000 **(b)** 100 000 **(c)** 100 000 000 **(d)** 1 000 000 000

....

2. Circle the expressions that are **not** in correct standard form.

4×10^5 0.4×10^{-3} 1.38×10^4 48×10^2

⑩ Standard form

Grade 5

1. What is 450 000 in standard form?

Circle your answer. **[1 mark]**

45×10^4 4.5×10^5 0.45×10^3 450×10^3

> Take out a factor that is a power of 10 to leave a number in the range $1 \leqslant A < 10$.

2. (a) Write 7.8×10^{-4} as an ordinary number. **[1 mark]**

 $7.8 \times 0.0001 =$ ....

....

(b) Work out $(3 \times 10^8) \div (5 \times 10^6)$. Give your answer in standard form. **[2 marks]**

 $(3 \div 5) \times (10^8 \div 10^6) =$ .... $\times 10^{\square}$

....

> **Exam focus** 📌
> A number in standard form is written as $A \times 10^n$, where $1 \leqslant A < 10$ and n is an integer.

> Make sure the first number lies in the range $1 \leqslant A < 10$.

3. Write these numbers in order of size. Start with the lowest number. **[3 marks]**

0.0045×10^6 45×10^{-4} -4.5×10^{-2} 4.5×10^5 45×10^3

....

⑩ Using standard form

Grade 5

4. One sheet of paper is 8×10^{-3} cm thick. Maria wants to put 1000 sheets of paper into the paper tray of her photocopier. The paper tray is 7.5 cm deep. Is the paper tray deep enough for 1000 sheets of this paper? Give a reason for your answer. **[3 marks]**

....

5. A satellite is travelling at a speed of 3460 metres per second. How many seconds will the satellite take to travel a distance of 4.75×10^{12} metres? Give your answer in standard form, correct to 3 significant figures. **[3 marks]**

> You may want to use this formula triangle:

.... s

 Made a start **Feeling confident** ☑ **Exam ready**

Surds

 Quick quiz

Work out

(a) $\sqrt{49}$ .... **(b)** $8 \times \sqrt{81}$ .... **(c)** $\sqrt{64} \times \sqrt{36}$ .... **(d)** $\sqrt{25} \times \sqrt{25}$ ....

 Surds 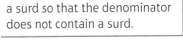 **Grades 7–8**

1. What is $\sqrt{32}$ written in its simplest form?

Circle your answer.   **[1 mark]**

$16\sqrt{2}$ $4\sqrt{2}$ $2\sqrt{8}$ $8\sqrt{2}$

> $32 = 16 \times 2$
>
> $16 = 4^2$

$\sqrt{32}$ is in its simplest form when the whole number under the square root sign is the smallest possible number.

2. Rationalise the denominator of $\dfrac{28}{\sqrt{7}}$.   **[2 marks]**

> $\dfrac{28}{\sqrt{7}} \times \dfrac{\square}{\sqrt{7}} = \dfrac{\square}{\square} = $ ....

....

Exam focus
To rationalise means to simplify a surd so that the denominator does not contain a surd.

Multiply top and bottom by $\sqrt{7}$.

3. Expand and simplify $(2 + \sqrt{3})(4 - \sqrt{3})$. Give your answer in the form $a + b\sqrt{3}$ where a and b are integers.   **[3 marks]**

Multiply out the brackets.

> $(2 + \sqrt{3})(4 - \sqrt{3}) = 2 \times 4 - 2\sqrt{3} + 4\sqrt{3} - $ ....

....

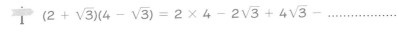 **Using surds** **Grade 9**

4. *ABD* is a right-angled triangle. All measurements are given in centimetres.

$AB = BD = \dfrac{\sqrt{3}}{3}$ and $BC = \dfrac{\sqrt{2}}{3}$.

Work out the exact area, in cm², of the shaded region.   **[3 marks]**

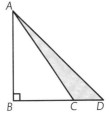

.... cm²

5. The diagram shows a rectangle *ABCD*.
The area of the rectangle is $1\,\text{m}^2$. The length of *AB* is $(1 + \sqrt{2})$ m.
Work out the perimeter of *ABCD*.
Give your answer in the form $a\sqrt{b}$ where a and b are integers.   **[4 marks]**

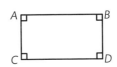

.... m

Number

 Factors and multiples   **Grade 5**

1. Rohan is planning his birthday party. He wants to buy some bottles of orange juice and bars of chocolate.

Orange juice	Chocolate
There are 8 bottles in a case. A case costs £4.50.	There are 6 bars in a packet. A packet costs £2.75.

He wants to buy exactly the same number of bottles of orange juice as bars of chocolate, but needs at least 70 of each. Work out the smallest amount that he will need to spend.   **[5 marks]**

£..............................

 Percentages   **Grade 6**

2. Anjali invests £8400 for 4 years.
The investment gets compound interest of x% per annum. At the end of 4 years the investment is worth £10 017.16.
Work out the value of x.   **[3 marks]**

....

 Surds   **Grade 7**

3. Alan rationalises the denominator of $\dfrac{6}{\sqrt{3}}$. His answer is $3\sqrt{3}$. Is Alan correct?

Tick a box.

Yes ☐   No ☐

Give a reason for your answer.   **[2 marks]**

....

....

 Bounds   **Grade 9**

4. Cecily is carrying out an experiment to see how a sledge slides down a hill.
The sledge starts from point X. The acceleration, a m/s² of the sledge is given by
$a = \dfrac{2s}{t^2}$ where s is the distance travelled in metres and t is the time taken in seconds.

Cecily finds that $s = 44.7$ metres, correct to 1 decimal place and $t = 5.86$ seconds, correct to 3 significant figures.

By considering bounds, work out the value of a to a suitable degree of accuracy. Give a reason for your answer.   **[5 marks]**

> Work out the upper bound and lower bound of s and t.

> **Exam focus**
> If an answer is given to a suitable degree of accuracy, the upper and lower bounds will both round to that value.

....

....

Algebraic expressions

1. Simplify

(a) $12x - 7x + 9x$

(b) $4(x - 5)$.

....

....

2. Factorise

(a) $x^2 + 4x$

(b) $x^2 - 9$.

....

....

 Simplifying, expanding and factorising **Grade 5**

1. Simplify $4x - 5y - 6x + 8y$.
Circle your answer. **[1 mark]**

$10x - 13y$ $3y - 2x$ $2x + 3y$ $-2x - 3y$

2. Factorise fully $4x^2 - 6x$. **[2 marks]**

$4x^2 - 6x = ... x(........ x - ....)$

....

3. Expand and simplify $(2x - 3)(3x + 7)$. **[2 marks]**

$(2x - 3)(3x + 7) = ... x^2 + ... x - ...... x - ......$

....

Look for the HCF of $4x^2$ and $6x$.

4. Expand and simplify

(a) $7x + 4(x - 2y) - 2(3x - 4y)$ **[2 marks]**

....

(b) $(x + 4)(x - 8)$ **[2 marks]**

....

(c) $(n + 3)^2 + (n - 2)^2$. **[2 marks]**

....

5. Factorise fully

(a) $15x^3y - 18xy^2$ **[2 marks]**

....

(b) $15x^4y^5 - 35x^2y^3$ **[2 marks]**

....

(c) $2ax - 2ay + bx - by$. **[3 marks]**

....

 Application **Grade 6**

6. (a) Show that $(n + 4)^2 - (n - 4)^2$ is an even number for all positive integer values of n. **[3 marks]**

(b) Prove algebraically that the difference between the squares of any two consecutive integers is equal to the sum of these two integers. **[4 marks]**

Two consecutive numbers are written as n and $n + 1$.

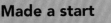 **Made a start** **Feeling confident** **Exam ready**

Algebraic formulae

BBC

---

⑤ Quick quiz

1. Expand and simplify

(a) $x(x + 6)$

(b) $(x + 2)(x - 3)$

....

....

2. Rearrange this equation so that the height, h, is the subject: $A = \frac{1}{2}bh$.

....

3. Write down the perimeter of each shape in terms of x.

(a)

(b)

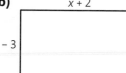

....

....

---

⑩ Deriving expressions

Grades 5–6

1. A shop sells packets of cards in two sizes. There are 6 cards in a small packet and 15 cards in a large packet.
The total number of cards in x small packets and y large packets is T. Write down a formula for T in terms of x and y.

[3 marks]

$T = $..........................

2. This shape is a solid prism.
The cross-section of the prism is an isosceles trapezium.
All the measurements are given in cm.
Show that the total surface area of the prism is $(74x^2 + 70x - 6)\,\text{cm}^2$.

> Work out the area of each face, then add up the areas of all the faces to find the total surface area.

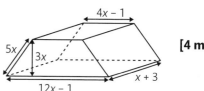

[4 marks]

---

⑩ Working out area

Grade 6

3. In the diagram, all measurements are in centimetres.
All the corners are right angles.
The area of the whole shape is A cm^2.
Write a formula for A in terms of x.
Give your answer in its simplest form.

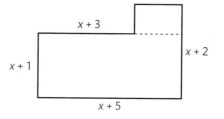

[4 marks]

> Split the compound shape into two rectangles.
> Then, work out the area of each rectangle.

➤ Height of small rectangle

$= (x + 2) - (\ldots + \ldots)$

$= \ldots + \ldots - \ldots - \ldots$

$= \ldots$

Width of small rectangle

$= (x + 5) - (\ldots + \ldots)$ | Multiply out brackets.

$= \ldots + \ldots - \ldots - \ldots$

$= \ldots$

Area of small rectangle $= \ldots \times \ldots = \ldots$

Area of large rectangle $= (x + 1)(\ldots + \ldots)$

$= \ldots + \ldots + \ldots + \ldots$

$= \ldots + \ldots + \ldots$

Area of whole shape $= \ldots + \ldots + \ldots + \ldots$

$= \ldots + \ldots + \ldots$

Exam focus 📌
Always leave your answer in its simplest form.

$A = $..........................

Made a start ☐ Feeling confident ☐ Exam ready ☐

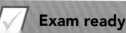

Laws of indices

② Quick quiz

Simplify fully

(a) $a \times a \times a \times a$

(b) $\dfrac{a \times a \times a \times a \times a \times a}{a \times a}$

(c) $6 \times a \times 3 \times a \times b$

(d) $3 \times a \times a \times b \times b \times b$.

....

⑤ Applying laws of indices Grade 5

1. (a) Simplify $x^7 \div x^3$. **[1 mark]**

....

> When you divide, subtract the powers.

(b) Simplify $6x^4y^3 \times 3x^2y$. **[2 marks]**

> When you multiply, add the powers.

$= 6 \times \text{.......} \times x^{\text{.......}} \times y^{\text{.......}}$

....

> Multiply or divide any numbers first, then use the laws of indices to work out the new powers.

(c) Simplify $(3x^2y^3)^3$. **[2 marks]**

$= 3x^2y^3 \times 3x^2y^3 \times 3x^2y^3$

....

(d) Simplify fully $\dfrac{15x^6y^4}{3x^4y}$. **[2 marks]**

Exam focus

Make sure you learn the laws of indices.

$= (15 \div \text{.......}) \times x^{\text{.......}} \times y^{\text{.......}}$

....

⑩ Indices with algebra   Grade 5

2. Simplify each expression fully.

(a) $3x^2y \times 5xy^3$ **[2 marks]**

> Multiply the numbers first.

(c) $\dfrac{20x^7y^3}{4x^2y}$ **[2 marks]**

....

(b) $\dfrac{20x^5(x+1)^3}{12x(x+1)}$ **[2 marks]**

> Cancel the numbers first.

(d) $(2x^6y^4)^4$ **[2 marks]**

....

....

⑩ Indices with equations   Grade 6

3. Work out the value of n, given that $\dfrac{t^7 \times t^n}{t} = t^{10}$.

[2 marks]

> Use the laws of indices to set up an equation.

4. Work out the value of x when

(a) $2^{20} \div 8^{12} = 2^x$ **[2 marks]**

$x = \text{........}$

(b) $3^{10} \times 27^4 \div 9 = 3^x$ **[2 marks]**

$n = \text{........}$ $x = \text{........}$

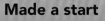

Combining indices

② Quick quiz

Evaluate

(a) $\sqrt{25} =$ ....

(b) $\sqrt{81} =$ ....

(c) $\sqrt[3]{27} =$ ....

(d) $\sqrt[3]{64} =$ ....

⑩ Negative and fractional indices

Grade 7

1. Simplify $3^6 \times 3^4$.
Circle your answer. **[1 mark]**

6^{10} 3^{10} 3^{24} 9^{24}

2. Evaluate 2^{-3}. **[1 mark]**

....

> When the power is negative, write the number as a fraction and invert it. Change the negative power to a positive power.

3. Evaluate

(a) $16^{\frac{3}{2}}$ **[1 mark]**

(b) $64^{\frac{2}{3}}$ **[1 mark]**

(c) $27^{\frac{2}{3}}$. **[1 mark]**

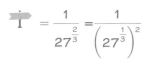 $= \left(16^{\frac{1}{2}}\right)^3$

....

> Split the power into the product of a unit fraction and an integer.

4. Evaluate

(a) $27^{-\frac{2}{3}}$ **[2 marks]**

(b) $81^{-\frac{1}{4}}$ **[2 marks]**

(c) $4^{-\frac{3}{2}}$. **[2 marks]**

📍 $= \dfrac{1}{27^{\frac{2}{3}}} = \dfrac{1}{\left(27^{\frac{1}{3}}\right)^2}$

> Always apply the laws of indices one step at a time.

....

5. Evaluate

(a) $\left(\dfrac{16}{81}\right)^{\frac{3}{4}}$ **[2 marks]**

(b) $\left(\dfrac{25}{4}\right)^{-\frac{3}{2}}$ **[2 marks]**

(c) $\left(\dfrac{27}{8}\right)^{-\frac{2}{3}}$. **[2 marks]**

📍 $= \left(\dfrac{4}{25}\right)^{\frac{3}{2}} = \left(\dfrac{4^{\frac{1}{2}}}{25^{\frac{1}{2}}}\right)^3$

Exam focus
Always use brackets to make your working clear, especially when using negative powers.

....

⑩ Solving equations involving indices

Grade 9

6. Solve the equations.

(a) $5^n = 1$ **[1 mark]**

(b) $5^n = \dfrac{1}{25}$ **[1 mark]**

(c) $3^{2n} = \dfrac{1}{81}$ **[2 marks]**

(d) $3^n = 9 \times \sqrt{27}$ **[2 marks]**

$n =$ .... $n =$ .... $n =$ .... $n =$ ....

Linear equations

5 Quick quiz

Rearrange $3p = \dfrac{y}{x}$ to make x the subject.

Circle your answer.

$x = \dfrac{3y}{p}$ $\qquad$ $x = \dfrac{3p}{y}$ $\qquad$ $x = \dfrac{y}{3p}$ $\qquad$ $x = \dfrac{yp}{3}$

15 Solving equations $\hspace{4cm}$ Grades 4–5

1. Solve these equations.

(a) $6x + 7 = 18$ **[2 marks]**

 $6x = 18 -$ ....

$6x =$ ....

Apply inverse operations to each step to collect all x terms on one side and numbers on the other.

$x =$ ....

(b) $9x + 6 = 2x - 19$ **[3 marks]**

$9x -$ .... $= -19 -$ ....

$x =$ ....

(c) $7(x + 2) = 21$ **[2 marks]**

$7x +$ .... $= 21$

$x =$ ....

(d) $4(y - 7) = 2(4 - y)$ **[3 marks]**

$4y -$ .... $=$ .... $-$ ....

$y =$ ....

(e) $4 - 3x = 11$ **[2 marks]**

$x =$ ....

(f) $5x - 14 = 2(3 + 2x)$ **[3 marks]**

$x =$ ....

2. (a) Solve $3(5 - 2x) - 2(2x + 3) = 2$. **[3 marks]**

$x =$ ....

(b) Solve $2(3x + 2) - 5(x - 2) = 4(x - 1)$. **[3 marks]**

$x =$ ....

10 Applying algebra to problems $\hspace{3cm}$ Grade 5

3. Company A sent x employees on a diversity course.
Company B sent three times as many employees as Company A.
Company C sent 9 fewer employees than Company A. The cost for the diversity course was £25 for each employee. Altogether, the companies paid a total of £2150.
Work out how many employees each company sent on the diversity course.
You **must** show your working.

Write out an equation in terms of x.

[5 marks]

....

4. Arianne and Betty are selling plates in a shop. They sell boxes of plates and single plates.
Arianne sells 6 boxes of plates and 32 single plates. Betty sells 5 boxes of plates and 4 single plates. Altogether, Arianne sells twice as many plates as Betty.
Work out how many plates there are in a box. You **must** show your working.

Let y represent the number of plates in a box.

[4 marks]

....

Linear equations and fractions

② Quick quiz

Solve

(a) $2x - 1 = 9$

(b) $\dfrac{x}{3} - 1 = 5$.

....

....

20 Solving equations with fractions　　　　Grade 7

1. Solve $\dfrac{x+1}{2} + \dfrac{2x-1}{3} = \dfrac{5}{6}$.　　**[4 marks]**

> Get rid of the fractions before you solve the equation.

$$\dfrac{6(x+1)}{2} + \dfrac{6(2x-1)}{3} = \dfrac{6 \times 5}{6}$$

$\ldots(x+1) + \ldots(2x-1) = \ldots$

$\ldots x + \ldots + \ldots x - \ldots = \ldots$

$\ldots x + \ldots = \ldots$

$\ldots x = \ldots - \ldots$

$\ldots x = \ldots$

$x = \ldots$

> Multiply every term by the lowest common denominator, which is the lowest common multiple (LCM) of the denominators.

Exam focus
Every line of working should include an equals sign and must be simplified step-by-step.

$x = \ldots$

2. Solve $x - 5 + \dfrac{2x-1}{4} = 3$.　**[4 marks]**

3. Solve $\dfrac{3}{2x-5} = \dfrac{2}{3x-2}$.　**[3 marks]**

$x = \ldots$

$x = \ldots$

4. Solve $\dfrac{5}{x+2} = \dfrac{9}{x-2}$.　**[5 marks]**

5. Solve $\dfrac{7}{x-2} - \dfrac{2}{x+1} = 0$.　**[5 marks]**

$x = \ldots$

$x = \ldots$

⑤ Solving algebraic equations in context　　　　Grade 8

6. A group of people play the lottery in a pool. One week, they win a prize and decide to share it equally between the 205 people in the group.
Before the prize can be shared, they discover that 5 people in the group did not pay for their share of the tickets, so the group decides instead to share the prize equally between the remaining 200 people. They discover that this means they will get an extra £2 each.
Let £x be the amount of the prize. Form an equation and solve it to find x.　**[6 marks]**

....

☑ **Made a start**　☑ **Feeling confident**　☑ **Exam ready**

Simultaneous equations

---

③ Quick quiz

Solve the simultaneous equations.

(a) $x = 6$

$2x - 3y = 0$

....

(b) $x = -1$

$4x + 10y = 5$

....

---

⑩ Algebraic method **Grade 5**

1. Solve the simultaneous equations. **[3 marks]**

$3x - 8y = 11$ (1)

| Start by numbering each equation. |

$2x - 5y = 6$ .... (2)

........$x -$ ....$y =$ .... (1) × 2

........$x -$ ....$y =$ .... (2) × 3

.... (2) from (1)

........$y =$ ....

$y =$ ....

> Substitute $y = $ .... into (1)
>
> $3x - 8(........) = 11$
>
> Rearrange for x
>
> ....
>
> ....

> Multiply one or both of the equations so that the coefficients of one unknown are the same.

> Substitute the value for this unknown into one of the original equations to find the other unknown.

Exam focus

Check the answer by substituting both unknowns into the unused original equation.

2. Solve the simultaneous equations **[4 marks]**

$x - 15 = 5y$

$3x + 8y = -1$

....

---

⑤ Graphical method **Grade 5**

3. Use a graphical method to solve the simultaneous equations $3x - y = 9$ and $x - 2y = -2$. **[3 marks]**

> When drawing a straight line, always choose three values of x and work out the corresponding y values.

> Plot the three points and draw a straight line through all of them.

....

Setting up equations **Grade 5**

4. The total cost of 4 shirts and 3 pairs of trousers is £104.
The total cost of 5 shirts and 2 pairs of trousers is £98.50.
Work out the cost of each shirt and each pair of trousers.

> Set up two equations.

[4 marks]

....

☑ **Made a start** ☑ **Feeling confident** ☑ **Exam ready** **19**

Quadratic equations

Quick quiz

Fill in the brackets so that the same two numbers make the given product and sum.

(a) $(\dots\dots) \times (\dots\dots) = 20$

$(\dots\dots) + (\dots\dots) = 12$

(b) $(\dots\dots) \times (\dots\dots) = -15$

$(\dots\dots) + (\dots\dots) = 2$

(c) $(\dots\dots) \times (\dots\dots) = 4$

$(\dots\dots) + (\dots\dots) = -5$

(d) $(\dots\dots) \times (\dots\dots) = -20$

$(\dots\dots) + (\dots\dots) = -1$

Solving quadratic equations
    Grade 7

1. Solve

(a) $2x^2 - 8x = 0$ **[2 marks]**

$2x(x - \dots\dots) = 0$

(b) $x^2 - 11x + 10 = 0$ **[2 marks]**

$(\dots\dots) \times (\dots\dots) = 10$

$(\dots\dots) + (\dots\dots) = -11$

$(x\dots\dots)(x\dots\dots) = 0$

(c) $9x^2 + 18x - 7 = 0.$ **[2 marks]**

$9x^2 + 21x - \dots\dots x - 7 = 0$

$3x(\dots x + \dots) - 1(\dots x + \dots) = 0$

....

Solving quadratic equations
    Grades 7–9

2. Solve

(a) $x^2 - 5x - 36 = 0$ **[2 marks]**

(b) $x^2 - 8x + 15 = 0.$ **[2 marks]**

> To answer this type of question, you have to rearrange the equation into the form $ax^2 + bx + c = 0$.

....

3. Solve

(a) $12x^2 - 5x - 7 = 5 + 2x$ **[3 marks]**

(b) $(3x - 1)^2 = 64.$ **[3 marks]**

....

Using quadratic equations
    Grade 8

4. *ABCD* is a square and *EFG* is a right-angled triangle. All measurements are in centimetres.   **[5 marks]**

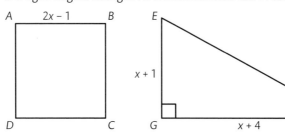

> Work out the area of the square and the triangle, then set up an equation.

The area of the square *ABCD* is equal to the area of the triangle *EFG*.
Work out the value of *x*. You **must** show your working.

....

Mixed simultaneous equations

⑤ Quick quiz

Write each equation in the form $ax^2 + bx + c = 0$.

(a) $x^2 - 3x = 7x - 6$

(b) $2x^2 - 8 = x^2 + 5x$

(c) $-3x^2 - x = -2x^2 + 3x - 10$

....

....

....

⑮ Algebraic method

Grades 8–9

1. Solve the simultaneous equations $y = x^2 - 3x + 9$ and $y = 2x + 3$. **[5 marks]**

$x^2 - 3x + 9 = 2x + 3$

$x^2 - \ldots x + \ldots = 0$

As both equations have y as the subject, set the RHSs equal.

$(x - \ldots)(x - \ldots) = 0$

$x = \ldots$ or $x = \ldots$

When $x = \ldots$, $y = 2(\ldots) + 3 = \ldots$

When $x = \ldots$, $y = 2(\ldots) + 3 = \ldots$

Solve the quadratic equation and then substitute the x-values into the linear equation to find the values of y.

....

2. Solve the simultaneous equations $x + 2y = -3$ and $x^2 - 2xy = 20$. **[5 marks]**

Always rearrange the linear equation and then substitute into the quadratic equation.

....

3. Solve the simultaneous equations $x + 2y = 4$ and $x^2 - 2y^2 = 2$. **[5 marks]**

....

⑩ Graphical method

Grade 8

4. Use a graphical method to solve the simultaneous equations $x^2 + y^2 = 25$ and $x + y = 1$. **[3 marks]**

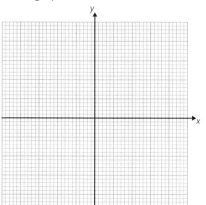

....

✓ **Made a start** ✓ **Feeling confident** ✓ **Exam ready**

Completing the square

② Quick quiz

Evaluate each expression.

(a) $-3^2 + 10$

(b) $-5^2 - 15$

(c) $-\left(\dfrac{3}{2}\right)^2 + 5$

(d) $-\left(\dfrac{7}{2}\right)^2 - 2$

....

⑩ Completing the square — Grade 8

1. The expression $x^2 + 10x - 8$ can be written in the form $(x + a)^2 + b$ for all values of x.

Work out the value of a and the value of b. **[2 marks]**

$x^2 + 10x - 8 = (x + \ldots\ldots)^2 - \ldots\ldots^2 - 8$

$a = \ldots\ldots, b = \ldots\ldots$

Use this formula to complete the square:

$$x^2 \pm 2bx + c = (x \pm b)^2 - b^2 + c$$

Exam focus

If the question includes $(x - a)^2 + b$, you need to complete the square.

2. The expression $x^2 - 4x + 5$ can be written in the form $(x - p)^2 + q$ for all values of x.

Work out the value of p and the value of q. **[2 marks]**

$p = \ldots\ldots, q = \ldots\ldots$

3. The expression $x^2 - 5x + 3$ can be written in the form $(x - p)^2 + q$ for all values of x.

Work out the value of p and the value of q. **[2 marks]**

$p = \ldots\ldots, q = \ldots\ldots$

⑤ Working out the turning points — Grade 8

4. The expression $x^2 - 8x + 18$ can be written in the form $(x - p)^2 + q$ for all values of x.

(a) Work out the value of p and the value of q. **[2 marks]**

$p = \ldots\ldots, q = \ldots\ldots$

The graph of $y = x^2 - 8x + 18$ has a minimum point.

(b) Write down the coordinates of this point. **[2 marks]**

....

5. $x^2 - 12x + 25 \equiv (x - a)^2 + b$

(a) Work out the value of a and the value of b.

[3 marks]

$a = \ldots\ldots, b = \ldots\ldots$

(b) What is the minimum value of $x^2 - 12x + 25$?

[2 marks]

....

⑤ Giving equations from turning points — Grade 8

6. The equation of a curve is $f(x) = x^2 + ax + b$. The diagram shows a sketch of part of the graph of $y = f(x)$. The coordinates of the turning point M are $(-3, 5)$.
Find the value of a and the value of b. **[3 marks]**

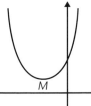

....

☑ **Made a start** ☑ **Feeling confident** ☑ **Exam ready**

The quadratic formula

 Quick quiz

Work out the value of $b^2 - 4ac$ when

(a) $a = 2$, $b = 3$ and $c = 4$ **(b)** $a = 3$, $b = -4$ and $c = -8$ **(c)** $a = 4$, $b = -6$ and $c = 5$ **(d)** $a = 1$, $b = 5$ and $c = -10$.

....

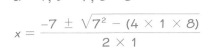 **Using the formula** **Grade 8**

1. Solve $x^2 + 7x + 8 = 0$.
Give your solutions to 2 decimal places. **[3 marks]**

 $a = 1$, $b = 7$, $c = 8$

$$x = \frac{-7 \pm \sqrt{7^2 - (4 \times 1 \times 8)}}{2 \times 1}$$

Use the quadratic formula $x = \dfrac{-b \pm \sqrt{b^2 - 4ac}}{2a}$

where a, b and c are constants in the general form $ax^2 + bx + c = 0$.

Exam focus

When you are asked to solve a quadratic equation to a specified degree of accuracy, always use the quadratic formula.

$x = \dots$ or $x = \dots$

2. Solve the equation $3x^2 + 6x = 2$.
Give your solutions to 2 decimal places. **[3 marks]**

3. Solve the equation $x^2 - 2x - 3 = x - 1$.
Give your solutions to 2 decimal places. **[3 marks]**

$x = \dots$ or $x = \dots$

$x = \dots$ or $x = \dots$

4. Solve $3x(2x - 1) = (x - 3)^2$.
Give your solutions to 3 significant figures. **[3 marks]**

5. Solve the equation $2(x - 4)^2 - 10(x - 3) = 14$.
Give your solutions to 2 decimal places. **[3 marks]**

$x = \dots$ or $x = \dots$

$x = \dots$ or $x = \dots$

 Using the formula in context **Grade 8**

6. The diagram shows a trapezium. All measurements are in centimetres.

The area of the trapezium is 64 cm². Work out the value of x.
Give your answer to 3 significant figures.
You **must** show your working.

Area of trapezium $= \dfrac{1}{2}(a + b)h$

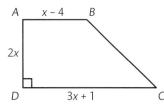

[5 marks]

$x = \dots$

Linear inequalities

① Quick quiz

Match each sign to the correct meaning.

<	>	⩽	⩾

greater than or equal to	less than	less than or equal to	greater than

⑩ Simple inequalities   Grade 5

1. Solve

(a) $4x - 5 > 19$ **[2 marks]**

$4x > 19 + 5$

$4x > ....$

....

(b) $6x \leqslant 2x - 18$ **[2 marks]**

$6x - .... \leqslant -18$

$....... x \leqslant ....$

....

(c) $10x + 4 > 3x + 25.$ **[3 marks]**

....

2. $-2 \leqslant x < 4$
Represent this inequality on the number line.   **[2 marks]**

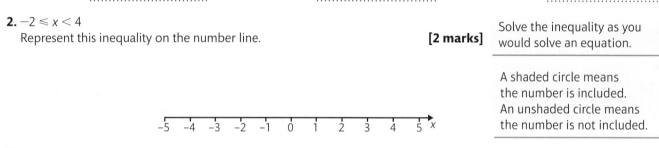

-5 -4 -3 -2 -1   0   1   2   3   4   5 x

> Solve the inequality as you would solve an equation.

> A shaded circle means the number is included. An unshaded circle means the number is not included.

⑮ Solving inequalities   Grade 6

3. Solve $\dfrac{4x - 3}{3} < \dfrac{2x - 1}{2}.$ **[2 marks]**

....

4. Write all the integers, x, that satisfy the inequalities $-4 \leqslant x < 3$ and $-3 < x < 7.$ **[2 marks]**

....

5. Helena is going to the bakery. She has £10. She wants to buy some buns for 32p each and some cakes for 45p each.

(a) Write down an inequality to show the number of buns and the number of cakes that Helena can buy.   **[2 marks]**

....

(b) Helena buys 14 buns. Work out the greatest number of cakes she can buy.   **[3 marks]**

....

6. If $3x + 6 > 19$, work out the smallest possible integer value of x.   **[3 marks]**

....

✓ **Made a start**   ✓ **Feeling confident**   ✓ **Exam ready**

Quadratic inequalities

⑤ Quick quiz

Factorise each expression.

(a) $x^2 - 3x$

(b) $x^2 + 6x + 8$

(c) $2x^2 + 7x - 4$

....

⑤ Simple quadratic inequalities   Grade 9

1. Solve $x^2 - 8x + 15 \geqslant 0$.   **[3 marks]**

🚩 $(......) \times (......) = 15$

$(......) + (......) = -8$

> Factorise and solve the quadratic equation.

> The x-values found are the critical values.

Exam focus 📌
Your final answer(s) must be given with inequality signs.

....

⑤ Harder quadratic inequalities   Grade 9

2. Solve $x^2 \leqslant 4(x + 8)$.   **[3 marks]**

3. Solve $(x - 2)^2 - 4(x + 1) > 0$.

Give your answer using set notation.   **[3 marks]**

....

⑩ Inequalities in context   Grade 9

4. A rectangular room has a width of x m. The room is 4 m longer than it is wide.

(a) Given that the perimeter of the room is greater than 12 m, show that $x > 1$.   **[3 marks]**

(b) Given also that the area of the room is less than 32 m²: **[4 marks]**
   (i) Write down an inequality, in terms of x, for the area of the room.

....

   (ii) Solve this inequality.

....

(c) Use your answers to parts (a) and (b) to find the range of possible values for x.   **[1 mark]**

....

Arithmetic sequences

Write down the next three terms in each sequence.

(a) 2   5   8

(b) 100   97   94

(c) 16   21   26

....

---

⑩ **The *n*th term** **Grade 5**

1. Which sequence is an arithmetic progression? Circle your answer. **[1 mark]**

1	3	8	12	17
1	3	4	7	11
1	3	27	81	243
1	4	7	10	13

> Work out the common difference and use this as the coefficient of *n*.

2. The first four terms of an arithmetic sequence are: 8   13   18   23

(a) Write an expression, in terms of *n*, for the *n*th term of this sequence. **[2 marks]**

🪧 *n*th term = ... *n* + ...

(b) The *n*th term of another sequence is $4n + 7$. Is 206 a term of this sequence?

You **must** show your working. **[2 marks]**

🪧 $4n + 7 = $ ....

....

> **Exam focus** 📌
> Once you have worked out the value of *n*, you can answer the question with 'yes' or 'no'.

3. The *n*th term of an arithmetic sequence is $3n + 4$, where *n* is a positive integer.

(a) Determine whether 110 is a term in this arithmetic sequence. **[2 marks]**

....

(b) Write an expression for the sum of the *n*th term and the $(n - 1)$th terms of this sequence.
Give your answer in its simplest form. **[2 marks]**

....

---

⑩ **The *n*th term for proofs** **Grade 5**

4. The *n*th term of sequence X is $4n - 3$. The *n*th term of sequence Y is $14 - 3n$.
Show that there is only one number that is in both sequences. Give a reason for your answer. **[3 marks]**

5. Here are the first five terms of an arithmetic sequence: 3   7   11   15   19
Prove that the difference between the squares of any two consecutive terms of the sequence is always a multiple of 8. **[5 marks]**

✓ **Made a start** ✓ **Feeling confident** ✓ **Exam ready**

Quadratic sequences

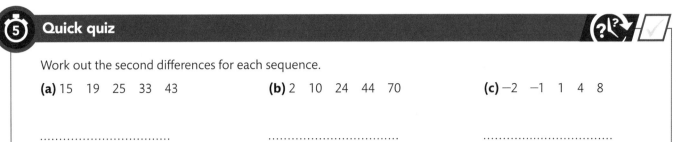

⑤ Quick quiz

Work out the second differences for each sequence.

(a) 15   19   25   33   43

(b) 2   10   24   44   70

(c) −2   −1   1   4   8

....

....

....

⑤ Geometric sequences

Grade 8

1. Circle the sequence that is a geometric progression.   **[1 mark]**

1	4	7	10	13
1	4	11	22	37
1	4	5	9	14
1	4	16	64	256

> In a geometric progression, the ratio of consecutive terms is constant.

⑮ Quadratic sequences

Grade 8

2. The first six terms of a sequence are: 5   11   19   29   41   55

> Set up a table to find the quadratic sequence.

Write an expression, in terms of n, for the nth term of this sequence.
You **must** show your working.   **[2 marks]**

n	1	2	3	4	5	6
n^2	1	4	9	16	25	36
$an^2 = \text{.......} n^2$						
u_n						
$u_n - an^2$						

....

3. The first four terms of a quadratic sequence are: 9   13   19   27

Write an expression, in terms of n, for the nth term of this quadratic sequence. You **must** show your working.   **[3 marks]**

....

4. Which sequence is a quadratic sequence? Tick a box.

☐ 5   8   11   14   ☐ 5   8   12.8   20.48   ☐ 5   8   14   23

Give a reason for your answer.   **[2 marks]**

....

....

5. The first five terms of a quadratic sequence are: 3   17   35   57   83
Write an expression, in terms of n, for the nth term of this quadratic sequence. You **must** show your working.   **[3 marks]**

....

Sequence problems

② Quick quiz

Write down the next three terms of each sequence.

(a) 100   98   96   94   92   **(b)** 1   4   9   16   25   **(c)** 1   1   2   3   5   **(d)** 2   4   8   16   32

....

⑤ Giving the nth term of a sequence   Grade 5

1. The nth term of a sequence is $an + b$ where a and b are integers.
The fourth term is 3 and the seventh term is -9.
Work out the value of a and the value of b.   **[3 marks]**

> Set up two simultaneous equations and solve them using the elimination method.

   $4a + b = 3$ and .... $a + b = $.......

$a = $......., $b = $.......

⑮ Different types of sequence   Grades 5–7

2. The first six terms of a Fibonacci sequence are:
1   3   4   7   11   18
(a) Give the 10th term of this sequence.

> The rule to continue a Fibonacci sequence is that each term (after the second in the sequence) is the sum of the two previous terms.

[1 mark]

....

(b) The first three terms of a different Fibonacci sequence are: a b $a + b$
Show that the 8th term of this sequence is $8a + 13b$.   **[2 marks]**

(c) Given that the 5th term is 13 and the 8th term is 55, find the value of a and the value of b.   **[3 marks]**

$a = $......., $b = $.......

3. The first three terms of a different Fibonacci sequence are: a $2b$ $a + 2b$
(a) Show that the 7th term of this sequence is $5a + 16b$.   **[2 marks]**

(b) Given that the 4th term is 14 and the 7th term is 58, work out the value of a and the value of b.   **[3 marks]**

$a = $......., $b = $.......

4. The nth term of a sequence is 3^n.
(a) Write down the first four terms of this sequence.   **[2 marks]**

....

(b) Work out the value of the 15th term in this sequence divided by the 11th term.   **[2 marks]**

....

Made a start   Feeling confident   Exam ready

Drawing straight-line graphs

 Quick quiz

1. Work out the gradient of the sloped line in this triangle.

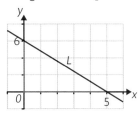

8

2

2. Given that $y = 3x + 1$, work out the value of y if

(a) $x = 4$ (b) $x = -5$.

....

 Working out the equation from graphs   **Grade 5**

1. Work out the equation of the straight line L.   **[3 marks]**

 $m = -\dfrac{\square}{\square}$

$c = \text{.......}$

y

6

L

0   5 x

....

Work out the gradient of the line by drawing a right-angled triangle with the line as the hypotenuse.

A line sloping down from left to right has a negative gradient.

Exam focus
Write the equation of the straight line as $y = mx + c$.

 Drawing straight-line graphs   **Grade 5**

2. On the grid, draw the graph of $y = 3x + 2$ for values of x from -2 to 2.   **[4 marks]**

3. On the grid, draw the graph of $y = 3 - 2x$ for values of x from -2 to 3.   **[4 marks]**

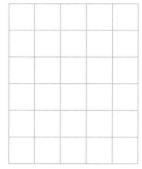

 Interpreting straight-line graphs   **Grade 5**

4. The graph gives information about the temperature of water and the length of time it has been heated.

(a) Interpret the value of the gradient.   **[3 marks]**

....

(b) Write the equation of the straight line.   **[1 mark]**

....

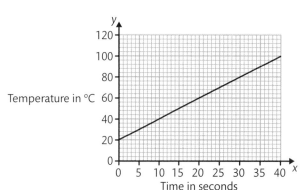

y

120
100
80
Temperature in °C 60
40
20
0
  0   5 10 15 20 25 30 35 40 x
           Time in seconds

Equations of straight lines

---

③ Quick quiz

1. (a) *A* is (3, 10) and *B* is (9, 4).

Circle the midpoint of *AB*.

(4, 5)   (5, 6)   (6, 7)   (7, 8)

(b) Tick (✓) the point that is not on the line $y = 3x + 2$.

☐ (0, 2)   ☐ (4, 14)   ☐ (2, 7)   ☐ (−1, −1)

---

⑳ Working out the equation   **Grade 5**

1. Work out an equation of the line with gradient −5 that passes through the point (3, 7).   **[2 marks]**

$$\ldots\ldots = \ldots\ldots \times \ldots\ldots + c$$

....

Exam focus 📌

Write the equation of the straight line as $y = mx + c$.

m is the gradient and c is the y-intercept. Substitute the gradient and the coordinates into $y = mx + c$ to find c.

2. The line *L* passes through the points (6, 17) and (2, 9). Work out an equation for the line *L*.   **[3 marks]**

....

3. *AB* is a line segment. The midpoint of line segment *AB* has coordinates (4, 5). Point *A* has coordinates (7, 3).

(a) Work out the coordinates of point *B*.   **[2 marks]**

....

(b) Work out an equation of the straight line that passes through *A* and *B*.   **[3 marks]**

....

4. L_1 is a straight line. The gradient of L_1 is 4. L_1 passes through the point (0, 8).
(a) Work out an equation of the straight line L_1.   **[2 marks]**

....

L_2 is a straight line. L_2 passes through the points with coordinates (1, −5) and (4, −3).
(b) Work out an equation of L_2.
Give your answer in the form $ay + bx = c$ where a, b and c are integers.   **[4 marks]**

....

☑ **Made a start**   ☑ **Feeling confident**   ☑ **Exam ready**

Parallel and perpendicular lines

3 Quick quiz

Circle the equation of a line that is parallel to $y = 6x - 4$.

$y = 4x - 6$ $y = 6x + 4$ $y = 2x - 4$ $y = -x - 4$

5 Working out equations of perpendicular lines   **Grades 5–6**

1. The straight line L has the equation $y = 2x - 3$.
   Work out the equation of the straight line that is perpendicular to L
   and passes through $(-3, 4)$.   **[3 marks]**

   If two lines are perpendicular, the product of their gradients is -1.

    $m = \text{.........}$ so the gradient of the perpendicular $= -\dfrac{\square}{\square}$

   Using $y = mx + c$ and the coordinates $(-3, 4)$, $4 = \text{.........} \times -3 + c$

   Exam focus
   Write the equation of the straight line in the form $y = mx + c$.

   $c = \text{....................}$

   ....

15 Using graphs and coordinates   **Grades 5–6**

2. The line L is drawn on this grid.

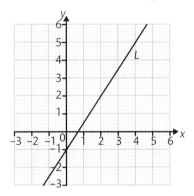

(a) Work out the equation of the straight line that is parallel to the line L and passes through $(0, 2)$.
[3 marks]

....

(b) Work out the equation of the straight line that is perpendicular to the line L and passes through $(1, 4)$.
[3 marks]

....

3. The straight line L has the equation $y = 3x - 7$.
   Work out the equation of a straight line that is perpendicular to L and passes through $(-3, 4)$.   **[3 marks]**

....

4. The straight line N goes through points $A(1, 1)$ and $B(4, -1)$. Is the line with equation $4y = 6x - 5$
   perpendicular to line N? You **must** show your working.   **[4 marks]**

....

5 Parallel lines   **Grade 5**

5. A and B are straight lines. Line A has equation $4y = 5x + 7$. Line B has equation $3y - 5x = 8$.
   Line C goes through the points $(-2, 3)$ and $(2, 8)$. Which two lines are parallel?
   You **must** show your working.   **[3 marks]**

....

Quadratic graphs

② Quick quiz

Match each equation to the correct graph.

$y = 3x - 2$	$y = x^2 - 6x - 7$	$y = 1 - 2x$	$y = 2 + 4x - x^2$

⑳ Drawing quadratic graphs

Grade 5

1. (a) Complete the table of values for $y = x^2 - 4x + 2$. **[2 marks]**

x	−1	0	1	2	3	4	5
y	7			−2			

Substitute the x-values into the equation to find the corresponding y-values.

(b) On the grid, draw the graph of $y = x^2 - 4x + 2$ for values of x from −1 to 5. **[3 marks]**

Always choose an appropriate scale so that you use the whole area of the graph to draw the curve.

Always draw a smooth curve. Never join the points with straight lines.

(c) Give estimates for the solutions of the equation $x^2 - 4x + 2 = 0$. **[2 marks]**

....

2. (a) Complete the table of values for $y = x^2 - 5x + 3$. **[2 marks]**

x	−1	0	1	2	3	4	5
y				−3			3

(b) On the grid, draw the graph of $y = x^2 - 5x + 3$ for values of x from −1 to 5. **[3 marks]**

(c) Give estimates for the solutions of the equation $x^2 - 5x + 3 = 0$. **[2 marks]**

....

3. (a) Complete the table of values for $y = 5 - x - x^2$. **[2 marks]**

x	−4	−3	−2	−1	0	1	2	3
y	−7				5			−7

(b) On the grid, draw the graph of $y = 5 - x - x^2$ for values of x from −4 to 3. **[3 marks]**

(c) Give estimates for the solutions of the equation $5 - x - x^2 = 0$. **[2 marks]**

....

Made a start ☑ Feeling confident ☑ Exam ready ☑

3.14

Cubic and reciprocal graphs

② Quick quiz

Match each equation with the correct graph.

$y = x^3$	$y = \dfrac{1}{x}$	$y = -\dfrac{1}{x}$	$y = -x^3$

⑳ Drawing cubic and reciprocal graphs

Grade 6

1. (a) Complete the table of values for $y = x + \dfrac{8}{x}$. **[2 marks]**

x	1	1.5	2	2.5	3	4	6	8
y		6.8			5.7			

Substitute the x-values into the equation to find the corresponding y-values.

(b) On the grid, draw the graph of $y = x + \dfrac{8}{x}$ for values of x from 1 to 8. **[3 marks]**

Choose an appropriate scale so that you use the whole graph area to draw the curve.

Always draw a smooth curve. Do not join up the points with straight lines.

(c) Give estimates for the solutions of the equation $x + \dfrac{8}{x} = 7$. **[2 marks]**

....

2. (a) Complete the table of values for $y = x^3 - 2x + 2$.
[2 marks]

x	-2	-1	0	1	2
y		3			

(b) On the grid, draw the graph of $y = x^3 - 2x + 2$ for values of x from -2 to 2. **[3 marks]**

(c) Give an estimate for the solution of the equation
$x^3 - 2x + 2 = 0$. **[2 marks]**

....

3. (a) Complete the table of values for $y = \dfrac{4}{x}$. **[2 marks]**

x	0.5	1	2	4	5	8
y		4			0.8	

(b) On the grid, draw the graph of $y = \dfrac{4}{x}$ for $0.5 \leqslant x \leqslant 8$. **[3 marks]**

Real-life graphs

Tick (✓) the correct answer.

(a) What does the gradient on a distance–time graph represent? ☐ acceleration ☐ speed

(b) How do you represent an object that is stationary on a distance–time graph? ☐ horizontal line ☐ vertical line

⑩ Distance–time graphs — Grade 5

1. Here is part of the travel graph of David's journey from his house to the airport and back.

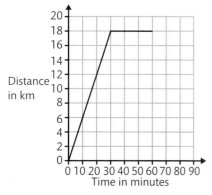

The gradient on a distance–time graph represents speed.

(a) Work out David's speed for the first 30 minutes of his journey. Give your answer in km/h. **[2 marks]**

$$Speed = \frac{18}{\boxed{}}$$

.... km/h

(b) At $t = 60$ minutes, David travels back to his house at 54 km/h. Complete the travel graph. **[2 marks]**

(c) How long does he spend at the airport? **[1 mark]**

.... minutes

2. Ravina walks along a path from her home to the town centre. Here is the distance–time graph for her journey from her home to the town centre.

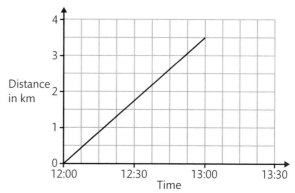

Mala leaves the town centre at 12:30 and walks at a constant speed along the same path to Ravina's home. She arrives at Ravina's home at 13:15.

(a) Show the information about Mala's journey on the graph. **[2 marks]**

(b) How far from Ravina's home were Ravina and Mala when they passed each other? **[1 mark]**

.... km

⑤ Real-life graphs — Grade 6

3. This graph can be used to convert between degrees Celsius (C) and degrees Fahrenheit (F).

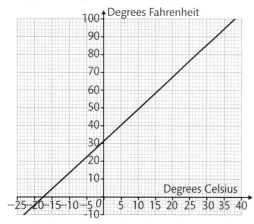

(a) Work out the equation for the straight line that gives F in terms of C. **[3 marks]**

....

(b) The temperature in Manchester is −4 °C. The temperature in New York is 40 °F. Where is it colder? **[1 mark]**

....

Trigonometric graphs

② Quick quiz

1. The sine graph is the .... shape as the cosine graph, but is translated to the right by .... °.

2. The sine graph and the cosine graph repeat themselves every .... °.

⑤ Using a sine graph — Grade 8

1. Here is a sketch of the curve $y = \sin x°$ for $0 \leqslant x \leqslant 360$.

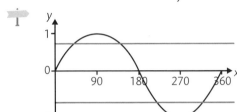

Given that $\sin 45° = \dfrac{\sqrt{2}}{2}$, write down the value of:

(a) $\sin 135°$ .... **[1 mark]**

(b) $\sin 225°$ .... **[1 mark]**

(c) $\sin 315°$ .... **[1 mark]**

Draw a straight horizontal line at $y = \dfrac{\sqrt{2}}{2}$.

Draw a straight horizontal line at $y = -\dfrac{\sqrt{2}}{2}$.

Exam focus

All the values above the x-axis are positive and all the values below the x-axis are negative.

⑩ Using a trigonometric graph — Grade 8

2. **(a)** Write down an exact value of x for which $\tan x = \sqrt{3}$. **[1 mark]**

.... °

(b) Sketch the graph of $y = \tan x$ for $0 \leqslant x \leqslant 360°$. **[2 marks]**

(c) Use your graph to work out one other value of x for which $\tan x = \sqrt{3}$. **[2 marks]**

.... °

3. **(a)** Write down an exact value of x for which $\sin x = \dfrac{\sqrt{3}}{2}$. **[1 mark]**

.... °

(b) Sketch the graph of $y = \sin x$ for $-360° \leqslant x \leqslant 360°$. **[2 marks]**

(c) Use your graph to work out two values of x for which $\sin x = -\dfrac{\sqrt{3}}{2}$. **[2 marks]**

.... ° and .... °

⑤ Using a cosine graph — Grade 8

4. The diagram shows the curve $y = \cos x$ for $0 \leqslant x \leqslant 360°$. Use the graph to work out estimates of the solutions, in the interval $0 \leqslant x \leqslant 360°$, of the equation:

(a) $\cos x = -0.3$ .... ° and .... ° **[2 marks]**

(b) $4 \cos x = 3$ .... ° and .... ° **[2 marks]**

(c) $2 + 5 \cos x = 4$. .... ° and .... ° **[2 marks]**

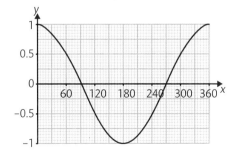

 Made a start    Feeling confident   Exam ready

Inequalities on graphs

Tick (✓) the correct answer.

(a) How is an inequality $<$ or $>$ represented on a graph? ☐ dashed line ☐ solid line

(b) How is an inequality $\leqslant$ or $\geqslant$ represented on a graph? ☐ dashed line ☐ solid line

⑮ Graphing an inequality   Grade 7

1. On the grid below show, by shading, the region defined by these inequalities:

$$x + y \leqslant 6 \qquad y > 2 \qquad x \geqslant -1$$

Mark this region with the letter R.   **[4 marks]**

> Draw the graphs of all three equations: $x + y = 6$, $y = 2$ and $x = -1$.

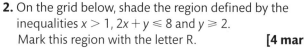

> Make sure you draw the correct type of line (solid or dotted) for each inequality sign.

Exam focus

Check your answer by choosing a point in the region and checking that its x- and y-coordinates satisfy **all three** inequalities.

2. On the grid below, shade the region defined by the inequalities $x > 1$, $2x + y \leqslant 8$ and $y \geqslant 2$. Mark this region with the letter R.   **[4 marks]**

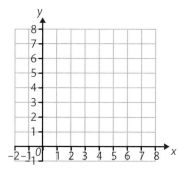

3. On the grid below, shade the region defined by the inequalities $x < 5$, $7x + 6y \geqslant 42$ and $y \leqslant 5$. Mark this region with the letter R.   **[4 marks]**

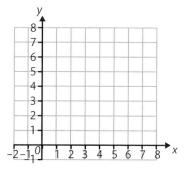

⑤ Inequalities from graphs   Grade 7

4. Write down inequalities to define the shaded region fully.   **[3 marks]**

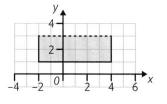

 Made a start 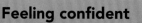 Feeling confident   Exam ready

Using quadratic graphs

Quick quiz ⑤

Match the equations. You will need to rearrange some of them.

| (a) $x^2 + 7x + 1 = 0$ |
| (b) $x^2 + 2x - 14 = 0$ |
| (c) $x^2 - 5x + 9 = 0$ |

| (i) $x^2 - 3x + 4 = 2x - 5$ |
| (ii) $x^2 + 6x + 5 = 4 - x$ |
| (iii) $x^2 + 5x - 11 = 3x + 3$ |

⑩ Simultaneous equations　　　　　　　　　　Grade 7

1. (a) Complete the table of values for $y = x^2 - 2x - 1$.　　　　　**[2 marks]**

x	−2	−1	0	1	2	3	4
y		2		−1			

$y = (-2)^2 - 2(-2) - 1 = \ldots$

$y = (0)^2 - 2(0) - 1 = \ldots$

$y = (1)^2 - 2(1) - 1 = \ldots$

$y = (\ldots)^2 - 2(\ldots) - 1$

Substitute the x-values into $y = x^2 - 2x - 1$ to find the corresponding y-values.

(b) On the grid, draw the graph of $y = x^2 - 2x - 1$ for values of x from −2 to 4.　　　**[3 marks]**

Exam focus

Points of intersection occur when two graphs cross each other. They are written as (x, y).

Choose an appropriate scale so that you use the whole graph to draw the curve of $y = x^2 - 2x - 1$.

Always draw a smooth curve and never join up the points with straight lines.

(c) On the same grid, draw the graph of $y = x + 3$.　　　　　**[1 mark]**

(d) Write down the points of intersection of $y = x^2 - 2x - 1$ and $y = x + 3$.　　　**[2 marks]**

....

⑩ Hidden linear equations　　　　　　　　　　Grade 7

2. (a) Complete the table of values for $y = x^2 - 3x + 2$.　　　**[2 marks]**

x	−1	0	1	2	3	4	5
y		2					12

(b) On the grid, draw the graph of $y = x^2 - 3x + 2$ for values of x from −1 to 5.　　　**[3 marks]**

(c) Use your graph to work out estimates for the solutions of the equation $x^2 - 4x + 1 = 0$.　　　**[2 marks]**

....

Turning points

② Quick quiz

Sketch a quadratic curve with the given line of symmetry.

Draw a dot at the turning point.

---

⑩ Working out a turning point **Grade 9**

1. (a) Write $x^2 - 10x + 3$ in the form $(x - b)^2 + c$, where b and c are integers.
[3 marks]

> $x^2 - 10x + 3 = (x - \ldots\ldots)^2 - \ldots\ldots^2 + 3$

....

> To give an answer in the form $(x - b)^2 + c$, complete the square.

> You can use this formula to complete the square:
>
> $x^2 \pm 2bx + c = (x \pm b)^2 - b^2 + c$

(b) Using your answer to part **(a)**, write down the coordinates of the turning point of the graph of $y = x^2 - 10x + 3$.
[1 mark]

Exam focus 📌

$(-b, c)$ gives the coordinates of the turning point.

....

2. (a) Write $2x^2 + 8x + 15$ in the form $a(x + b)^2 + c$, where a, b and c are integers.
[3 marks]

....

(b) Using your answer to part **(a)**, write down the coordinates of the turning point of the graph of $y = 2x^2 + 8x + 15$.
[1 mark]

....

---

⑩ Interpreting quadratic graphs **Grade 9**

3. Given that the minimum turning point of a quadratic curve is $(-4, -2)$, work out an equation of the curve in the form $y = x^2 + px + q$.
[3 marks]

....

4. (a) Write $2x^2 - 4x + 7$ in the form $a(x + b)^2 + c$.
[3 marks]

....

(b) Hence, or otherwise, explain why the graph of the curve with equation $y = 2x^2 - 4x + 7$ does not intersect the x-axis.
[1 mark]

....

5. The curve shown in the diagram has equation $x^2 + bx + c$, where b and c are constants. Find the exact coordinates of the points where the curve intercepts the x-axis.
[6 marks]

....

☑ **Made a start** ☑ **Feeling confident** ☑ **Exam ready**

Sketching graphs

Quick quiz

Solve these quadratics.

(a) $x^2 - 25 = 0$ .... **(b)** $x^2 - 9x + 20 = 0$ .... **(c)** $x^2 - 7x = 18$ ....

Completing the square **Grade 8**

1. (a) Show that $x^2 - 8x + 19$ can be written as $(x + p)^2 + q$ where p and q are integers to be found. **[2 marks]**

> To give an answer in the form $(x + p)^2 + q$, complete the square.

$x^2 - 8x + 19 = (x - \text{..........})^2 - \text{..........}^2 + 19$

....

> Determine whether the graph is ∪-shaped or ∩-shaped.

(b) Sketch the curve with equation $y = x^2 - 8x + 19$, showing clearly any intersections with the coordinate axes. **[2 marks]**

$y = (x - \text{..........})^2 + \text{..........}$

Exam focus

To find any intersections with the axes, you need to find the x-values when $y = 0$, and the y-values when $x = 0$.

Sketching graphs **Grade 9**

2. (a) Show that $x^2 - 8x + 12$ can be written as $(x + a)^2 + b$ where a and b are integers to be found. **[2 marks]**

3. (a) Factorise fully $x(x^2 - x - 12)$. **[2 marks]**

....

(b) Sketch the curve with equation $y = x^2 - 8x + 12$, showing the coordinates of the points at which the curve meets the axes. **[3 marks]**

(b) Sketch the curve with equation $y = x(x^2 - x - 12)$, showing the coordinates of the points at which the curve meets the x-axis. **[2 marks]**

4. Sketch the curve with equation $y = (x - 3)(x - 2)(x + 1)$, showing the coordinates of the points at which the curve meets the x-axis. **[3 marks]**

5. (a) Factorise $x^2 - 16$. **[1 mark]**

....

(b) Sketch the curve with equation $y = x^2 - 16$, showing the coordinates of the points at which the curve meets the axes. **[3 marks]**

Exponential graphs

② Quick quiz

Complete these sentences by crossing out the incorrect word or phrase.

(a) $x = 6000 \times 0.7^3$

This value of y is **increasing / decreasing** because 0.7 is **less than 1 / more than 1**.

(b) $x = 6000 \times 1.4^2$

This value of y is **increasing / decreasing** because 1.4 is **less than 1 / more than 1**.

⑩ Drawing exponential graphs — Grade 6

1. (a) Complete the table of values for $y = 2^x$. **[2 marks]**

x	−1	0	1	2	3	4
y				4		

(b) On the grid, draw the graph of $y = 2^x$ for values of x from −1 to 4. **[3 marks]**

Substitute the x-values into $y = 2^x$ to find the corresponding y-values.

Choose an appropriate scale so that you use the whole grid to draw the curve for $y = 2^x$.

⑩ Using exponential equations — Grade 6

2. On 1 January bacteria were introduced into a lake. The formula $V = 2^t$ gives the volume, V, of water containing bacteria after t days.

(a) Complete the table. **[2 marks]**

t	0	1	2	3	4	5	6
V		2		8			

(b) Draw the graph of $V = 2^t$. **[3 marks]**

At the same time, a pollutant leaked into the lake. The formula $P = 12 + t$ gives the volume of water P, containing pollutant after t days.

(c) On the same grid, draw the graph of $P = 12 + t$. **[1 mark]**

(d) After how many days was the volume containing bacteria equal to the volume containing pollutant? **[1 mark]**

....

Exam focus

Always draw a smooth curve through the points, never join up the points with straight lines.

Made a start   Feeling confident   Exam ready

Gradients of curves

1. Tick (✓) the correct statement.

The gradient of a curve is defined as: $\text{gradient} = \dfrac{\text{change in horizontal value}}{\text{change in vertical value}}$ ⬚ $\text{gradient} = \dfrac{\text{change in vertical value}}{\text{change in horizontal value}}$ ⬚

2. Work out the gradient of the hypotenuse in each triangle.

(a)

7

21

....

(b)

9

3

....

(15) **Gradients of non-linear graphs** | **Grade 9**

1. A liquid was poured into a barrel at a steady rate. The results are shown on the graph.

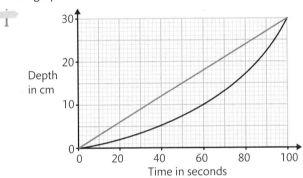

Depth in cm

Time in seconds

To find the average rate of increase, draw a line from (0, 0) to (100, 30). Work out the gradient of this line.

 Exam focus
A positive gradient means that the rate of change is increasing.

(a) Work out the average rate of increase of the depth of the water between $t = 0$ and $t = 100$.   **[2 marks]**

For part **(b)**, draw a tangent at $t = 60$ and work out its gradient.

.... cm/s

(b) Estimate the gradient of the curve when $t = 60$ seconds.   **[2 marks]**

.... cm/s

(c) Interpret your answer to part **(b)**.   **[1 mark]**

....

2. Robert bought an antique from an auction. The graph shows the value of the antique against the number of years he owns it for.

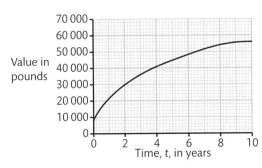

Value in pounds

Time, t, in years

(a) Work out the average rate of increase of the value of the antique between $t = 0$ and $t = 10$. State the units.   **[2 marks]**

....

(b) Estimate the rate of increase of the value of the antique at $t = 4$. State the units.   **[2 marks]**

....

Velocity–time graphs

 Quick quiz

Tick (✓) the correct box.

(a) What does the gradient on a velocity–time graph represent? distance travelled ⬚ speed ⬚ acceleration ⬚

(b) What does the area under a velocity–time graph represent? distance travelled ⬚ speed ⬚ acceleration ⬚

 Linear graphs   **Grade 9**

1. The graph shows how the velocity of a train varies as it moves along a straight railway line.

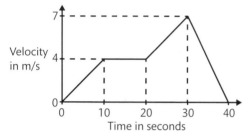

Work out the acceleration by finding the gradient of the velocity–time graph.

Exam focus
Work out the total distance by finding the area under the graph.

(a) Work out the acceleration of the train during the first 10 seconds of its motion. **[2 marks]**

(b) Work out the total distance, in metres, travelled by the train. **[3 marks]**

.... m/s²

.... m

 Non-linear graphs   **Grade 9**

2. Asha runs in a race. The graph shows her speed, in metres per second, t seconds after the start of the race.

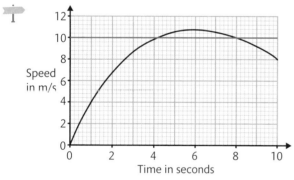

(a) Write down the time at which Asha's speed was greatest. **[1 mark]**

.... s

(b) Write down the times at which Asha's speed was 10 m/s. **[3 marks]**

Speed = 10 m/s at 4.2 seconds and

.... seconds.

(c) Work out the gradient when $t = 8$ and state what this represents. **[3 marks]**

....

3. The graph shows information about the velocity, v m/s, of a bungee jumper t seconds after she jumps off a crane.

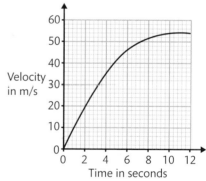

(a) Write down the speed of the bungee jumper at $t = 4$. **[2 marks]**

.... m/s

(b) Write down the time when the speed of the bungee jumper is 50 m/s. **[2 marks]**

.... s

(c) Work out the acceleration when $t = 4$. **[3 marks]**

.... m/s²

Made a start ✓ **Feeling confident** ✓ **Exam ready** ✓

Areas under curves

 ② Quick quiz

Find the area of this trapezium:

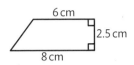

6 cm
2.5 cm
8 cm

.... cm²

⑤ Velocity–time graphs   Grade 9

1. Here is a velocity–time graph for a lorry.

(a) Use five equal intervals on the graph to estimate the total distance
travelled in the first 100 seconds.   **[4 marks]**

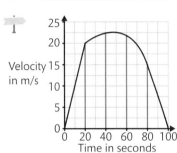

Velocity in m/s
25, 20, 15, 10, 5, 0
0 20 40 60 80 100
Time in seconds

Distance = [0.5 (0 + 20) × 20] + [0.5 (20 + 22.5) × 20] +
[0.5 (22.5 + 22) × 20] + [0.5 (22 + 15) × 20] +
[0.5 (15 + 0) × 20]

.... m

To find the total distance travelled, split the region into simple shapes.
Work out the area of each shape and add the areas together.

 Exam focus
'Justify your answer' means you must
show how you arrived at your conclusion.

(b) Is the answer to part **(a)** an overestimate or an underestimate?
Justify your answer.   **[1 mark]**

The answer is an .... -estimate because ....

....

⑮ Different types of graph   Grade 9

2. The graph shows the rate at which water is flowing in a pipe.

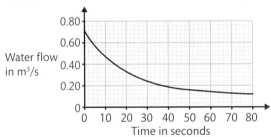

Water flow in m³/s
0.80, 0.60, 0.40, 0.20, 0
0 10 20 30 40 50 60 70 80
Time in seconds

(a) Use four equal intervals on the graph to estimate the
volume of water flowing in the first 80 seconds.
                    [4 marks]

.... m³

(b) Is the answer to part **(a)** an overestimate or an
underestimate? Justify your answer.   **[1 mark]**

....

....

3. The graph shows the amount of power, in kilowatts,
produced by a solar panel over a period of time, in hours.

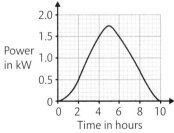

Power in kW
2.0, 1.5, 1.0, 0.5, 0
0 2 4 6 8 10
Time in hours

The area under a power–time graph represents the
amount of energy produced.

(a) Use six equal intervals on the graph to estimate the
amount of power produced between $t = 2$ and $t = 8$.
                    [4 marks]

.... kW

(b) Is the answer to part **(a)** an overestimate or an
underestimate? Justify your answer.   **[1 mark]**

....

....

Transforming graphs

② Quick quiz

Complete the sentences.

(a) A transformation of $y = -f(x)$ is a reflection in the .... axis.

(b) A transformation of $y = f(-x)$ is a reflection in the .... axis.

⑮ Reflecting and translating graphs   Grade 9

1. The curve with equation $y = x^2 + 6x - 1$ is reflected in the x-axis.

Circle the equation of the reflected curve.   **[1 mark]**

> Make sure you know the difference between reflections and translations.

$y = x^2 + 6x + 1$ $y = -x^2 + 6x - 1$ $y = -x^2 - 6x + 1$ $y = x^2 + 6x - 1$

2. The diagram shows part of the curve with equation $y = f(x)$.

The coordinates of the maximum point of the curve are (6, 15).

(a) Write down the coordinates of the turning point of the curve with equation:

(i) $y = f(x + 4)$ **[1 mark]**   **(ii)** $y = f(x) + 4$ **[1 mark]**

 Maximum point $= (6 - 4, 15)$

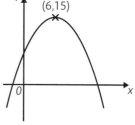

....

(iii) $y = f(-x)$ **[1 mark]**   **(iv)** $y = -f(x)$ **[1 mark]**

> $y = -f(x)$ is a reflection in the x-axis and $y = f(-x)$ is a reflection in the y-axis.

....

> $y = f(x \pm a)$ is a horizontal translation and $y = f(x) \pm a$ is a vertical translation.

(b) The curve with equation $y = f(x)$ is transformed to give the curve with equation $y = f(x) - 2$.
Describe the transformation.   **[1 mark]**

....

3. The two grids below both show the graph of $y = f(x)$. Sketch these translations on the grids.

(a) $y = -f(x)$ **[2 marks]**   **(b)** $y = f(x + 4)$ **[2 marks]**

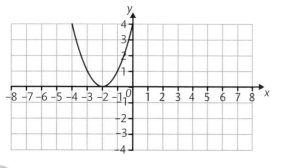   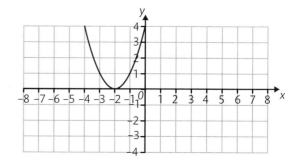

⑤ Using transformations to find coordinates   Grade 9

4. The graph of $y = f(x)$ is transformed to give the graph of $y = -f(x + 4)$. The point A on the graph of $y = f(x)$ is mapped to the point B on the graph of $y = -f(x + 4)$. The coordinates of point A are (10, 2). Work out the coordinates of point B. **[2 marks]**

....

 Made a start   Feeling confident   Exam ready

Algebraic fractions

 Quick quiz

Give the lowest common multiple for each set of values.

(a) 3 and 4 ....   **(c)** x and $(x+2)$ ....

(b) 4, 6 and 10 ....   **(d)** $(x-1)$ and $(x+5)$ ....

 Simplifying algebraic fractions   **Grades 7–8**

1. Simplify $\dfrac{x+1}{3} + \dfrac{x-4}{2}$.   **[3 marks]**

$$= \frac{2(x+1)}{6} + \frac{3(x-4)}{6} = \frac{2(x+1)+3(x-4)}{6}$$

$$= \frac{2 \times x + 2 \times \text{.......} + 3 \times \text{.......} + \text{.......} \times \text{.......}}{6}$$

....

> Work out the lowest common denominator first.

> **Exam focus**
> Always simplify your final answer.

2. Simplify $\dfrac{5}{x+3} + \dfrac{4}{x-1}$.   **[3 marks]**

3. Simplify $\dfrac{3}{4x} - \dfrac{2}{5x} + \dfrac{1}{3x}$.   **[2 marks]**

....

 Factorising numerators and/or denominators   **Grade 8**

4. Simplify $\dfrac{x^2 - 25}{x^2 - 11x + 30}$.   **[3 marks]**

5. Simplify $\dfrac{3x^2 + 2x - 8}{x^2 + x - 2}$.   **[3 marks]**

....

 Changing the subject of a formula   **Grade 7**

6. Make n the subject of the formula
$$m = \frac{3n}{n+2}.$$ **[3 marks]**

> First, multiply out the denominator.

 $m(n+2) = 3n$

7. Make x the subject of the formula
$$y = \frac{5x+4}{3-x}.$$ **[4 marks]**

....

 Applying arithmetical rules to algebraic fractions   **Grade 8**

8. Simplify fully $\dfrac{x^2 - 25}{2x^3} \div \dfrac{x^2 - x - 30}{4x}$.   **[4 marks]**

9. Write $10 + \left[(x+7) \div \dfrac{x^2 + 2x - 35}{x-3} \right]$ as a single fraction in its simplest form.
You **must** show your working.   **[4 marks]**

....

Quadratics and fractions

 ⑤ Quick quiz

Solve these equations.

(a) $x^2 + 13x + 36 = 0$ .... **(b)** $2x^2 + x - 15 = 0$ ....

㉕ Linear factors in the denominator   **Grade 9**

1. Solve $\dfrac{1}{x + 1} + \dfrac{3}{x + 3} = 2$.   **[5 marks]**

> Work out the lowest common denominator.

$$\frac{1(x + 3)}{(x + 1)(x + 3)} + \frac{3(x + 1)}{(x + 3)(x + 1)} = 2$$

> Simplify the numerator by multiplying out the brackets.

$$\frac{1(x + 3) + 3(x + 1)}{(x + 1)(x + 3)} = 2$$

$$1(x + 3) + 3(x + 1) = 2(\ldots\ldots\ldots\ldots)$$

....

2. Solve $\dfrac{3x - 2}{5x} - \dfrac{x - 2}{3x} = 4$.   **[4 marks]**

3. Solve $\dfrac{4}{2x - 1} = \dfrac{3}{4x - 1} + 3$.   **[5 marks]**

....

4. Solve $\dfrac{1}{2x + 3} + \dfrac{3}{x - 1} = \dfrac{2}{x - 3}$.   **[6 marks]**

5. Solve $\dfrac{1}{x - 2} - \dfrac{2}{x + 1} = \dfrac{1}{x - 1}$.   **[6 marks]**

....

 Made a start   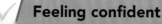 **Feeling confident**   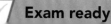 **Exam ready**

Function notation

⑤ Quick quiz

1. Given that $f(x) = 3x + 2$, work out the value of $f(x)$ when   **(a)** $x = 3$ ....   **(b)** $x = -4$. ....

2. Solve these equations.   **(a)** $3x + 4 = 10$ ....   **(b)** $x^2 + 13x + 40 = 0$ ....

⑳ Manipulating functions   Grades 7–8

1. $f(x) = 3 - 5x$ and $g(x) = x^2$

(a) Work out

   (i) $f(0)$ **[1 mark]**

   $f(0) = 3 - 5(0)$

   ....

   (ii) $f(-1)$.   **[1 mark]**

   $f(-1) = 3 - 5(..............)$

   ....

(b) Solve $gf(x) = 4$.   **[2 marks]**

   $(3 - ....)^2 =$

> When working with composite functions, the order of substitution is very important.

   ....

(c) Solve $fg(x) = 2x$.   **[3 marks]**

   ....

2. For all values of x, $f(x) = 3x - 4$ and $g(x) = 4x + 5$.

(a) Work out an expression for $fg(x)$.   **[2 marks]**

   $3(4x + 5) - 4 =$

> Substitute the given function $g(x)$ into $f(x)$.

   ....

(b) Solve $fg(x) = -25$.   **[2 marks]**

   $3(4x + 5) - 4 = -25$

> Use the answer to part (a) and solve for x.

   ....

> **Exam focus** 📌
> Always simplify the composite function to its simplest form.

3. For all values of x, $f(x) = x^2 + 2$ and $g(x) = 4x - 1$.

(a) Work out the value of $gf(-2)$.   **[1 mark]**

   ....

(b) Solve $fg(x) = gf(x)$.   **[4 marks]**

   ....

4. For all values of x, $f(x) = 2x + 1$ and $g(x) = 4 - x^2$.

(a) Solve $f(x) = g(x)$.   **[3 marks]**

   ....

(b) Solve $fg(x) = -24$.   **[3 marks]**

   ....

⑤ Functions and proof   Grade 9

5. The function f is defined by $f(x) = \dfrac{1}{1 - x}$ for $x \neq 1$. Prove that $ff(x) = \dfrac{x - 1}{x}$.   **[4 marks]**

6. The functions f, g and h are defined as $f(x) = 3 - x$, $g(x) = x^2 - 14$ and $h(x) = x - 2$.

Given that $f(x) = gfh(x)$, work out the values of x.   **[4 marks]**

   $x = ..., x = ...$

Inverse functions

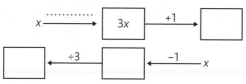

② Quick quiz

Complete the function machines.

x ⟶ | $3x$ | ⟶ +1 ⟶ | ☐ |

☐ ⟵ ÷3 ⟵ | ☐ | ⟵ −1 ⟵ x

⑩ Working out an inverse function **Grade 9**

1. Circle the expression that shows the inverse function of $f(x) = 3x + 5$. **[1 mark]**

$\dfrac{x-3}{5}$ $\dfrac{x-5}{3}$ $\dfrac{3-x}{5}$ $\dfrac{5-x}{3}$

2. (a) Work out the inverse function of $f(x) = \dfrac{3}{x-4}$. **[2 marks]**

3. $f(x) = 2x^2 + 3$ and $g(x) = \dfrac{3x}{2x-1}$

(a) Work out the inverse function of $g(x)$. **[3 marks]**

....

(b) Solve $f^{-1}(x) = 10$. **[2 marks]**

....

(b) Work out $gf(x)$. **[2 marks]**

....

....

⑩ Using inverse functions in equations **Grade 9**

4. The functions f and g are defined as
$f(x) = x^2$ and $g(x) = x - 3$.

(a) Give $gf(x)$. **[2 marks]**

5. f is the function $f(x) = 2x - 5$ and g is the function $g(x) = x^2 - 8$.

(a) Work out $f(3)$. **[1 mark]**

....

(b) Work out $fg(-5)$. **[2 marks]**

....

(b) Give the inverse function $g^{-1}(x)$. **[2 marks]**

(c) Work out the inverse of $f(x)$. **[2 marks]**

....

(c) Solve the equation $gf(x) = g^{-1}(x)$. **[2 marks]**

(d) Solve $gf(x) = 1$. **[4 marks]**

....

....

 Made a start **Feeling confident** 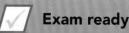 **Exam ready**

Equation of a circle

② Quick quiz

Complete the sentence by crossing out the incorrect equations.

The general equation of a circle is $y = mx + r$ / $y = ax^2 + bx + r$ / $x^2 + y^2 = r^2$, where r is the ....

⑤ Using the equation of a circle

Grade 9

1. Work out the diameter of the circle $x^2 + y^2 = 36$.

Circle your answer. **[1 mark]**

6   12   18   72

2. C is the circle with equation $x^2 + y^2 = 50$.

(a) Show that the point $(-1, -7)$ lies on C. **[1 mark]**

$(.......)^2 + (.......)^2 = ... + ... = 50$

(b) Write down the radius of the circle.
Give your answer in its simplest form. **[2 marks]**

$r^2 = ...$

....

> The equation of the circle is of the form $x^2 + y^2 = r^2$.

> Substitute the values of x and y into the equation.

> **Exam focus** 📌
> You can leave your answer in surd form.

⑮ Simultaneous equations

Grade 9

3. (a) Draw the graph of $x^2 + y^2 = 36$ on this grid. **[2 marks]**

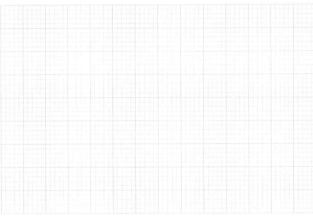

(b) Give estimates for the solutions of the simultaneous equations $x^2 + y^2 = 36$ and $y = x + 1$. **[2 marks]**

....

4. Solve the simultaneous equations $x^2 + y^2 = 14$ and $y = x + 3$. Give your answers to 3 significant figures. **[5 marks]**

> Substitute $y = x + 3$ into $x^2 + y^2 = 14$ and then rearrange to form a quadratic equation.

....

5. Solve the simultaneous equations $x^2 + y^2 = 20$ and $y = 3x + 2$. **[5 marks]**

....

6. The line L is a tangent to the circle $x^2 + y^2 = 65$ at the point A. A is the point $(-4, 7)$. Work out the equation of the line L. **[4 marks]**

....

Iteration

② Quick quiz

Using the values of x_1, x_2 and x_3, write down a solution for x correct to 2 decimal places.

(a) $x_1 = 1.795\,800$

$x_2 = 1.790\,02$

$x_3 = 1.791\,315$

(b) $x_1 = 0.410\,256$

$x_2 = 0.414\,896$

$x_3 = 0.414\,096$

(c) $x_1 = 3.617\,461$

$x_2 = 3.618\,101$

$x_3 = 3.618\,026$

....

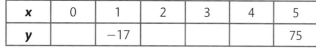
㉕ **Using iteration to find estimates**   Grade 9

1. (a) Complete the table for $y = x^3 - 8x - 10$.   **[1 mark]**

x	0	1	2	3	4	5
y		-17				75

> Substitute x-values into the equation to find the y-values.

(b) There is a solution to the equation $x^3 - 8x - 10 = 0$ between 2 consecutive integers. State these 2 integers.

Give a reason for your answer.   **[2 marks]**

> Look for where the y-values change from negative to positive.

....

....

(c) Show that the equation $x^3 - 8x - 10 = 0$ can be rearranged to give $x = \sqrt[3]{8x + 10}$.   **[2 marks]**

$x^3 = \ldots\ldots\ldots$

> Start by rearranging the equation for x^3.

(d) Use the iteration $x_{n+1} = \sqrt[3]{8x_n + 10}$, with $x_0 = 3.5$, to work out a solution to the equation $x^3 - 8x - 10 = 0$ to 2 decimal places.   **[3 marks]**

$x_1 = \ldots\ldots\ldots$

....

2. (a) Show that the equation $x^3 - 6x = -2$ has a solution between $x = 2$ and $x = 3$.   **[2 marks]**

3. (a) Show that the equation $x^2 + x - 3 = 0$ can be rearranged to give $x = \dfrac{3}{1 + x}$.   **[2 marks]**

(b) Show that the equation $x^3 - 6x = -2$ can be rearranged to work out $x = \sqrt[3]{6x - 2}$.   **[2 marks]**

(b) Use the iteration $x_{n+1} = \dfrac{3}{1 + x_n}$, with $x_0 = 1$, to work out the values of x_1, x_2 and x_3.   **[2 marks]**

(c) Use the iteration formula $x_{n+1} = \sqrt[3]{6x_n - 2}$, with $x_0 = 2.5$, to solve $x^3 - 6x = -2$ to 2 decimal places.   **[3 marks]**

....

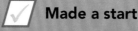 **Made a start**   **Feeling confident**    **Exam ready**

Algebra

Algebraic skills

1. (a) $f(x) = x^2 - 6x + 12$. Sketch a graph of $y = f(x)$, showing the coordinates of the turning point and the coordinates of any intercepts with the coordinate axes.
[4 marks]

> To find the coordinates of the turning point, you must complete the square.

> The minimum point on the graph is at $y = 3$, so there is only a y-axis intercept. Work out the value of the y-value when $x = 0$.

(b) Hence, or otherwise, determine whether $f(x + 2) - 4 = 0$ has any real roots. Give reasons for your answer.
[2 marks]

> $f(x + 2) - 4$ is a translation, so work out which way the graph moves.

....

2. $a(2x + 3) + b(7x + 8) \equiv 12x + 13$

Work out the values of a and b. You must use an algebraic method.
[6 marks]

$a = ...,\ b = ...$

3. The value of a van, in £, is given by $V = 30\,000 \times 0.8^t$ where t is the age of the van in complete years.

(a) Write down the value of the van when it was brand new.
[1 mark]

> It can be assumed that $t = 0$ when the van is brand new.

£ ....

(b) Explain how you know that the value of the van is decreasing.
[1 mark]

....

(c) Work out the value of the van when it is 5 years old.
[2 marks]

£ ....

(d) After how many years will the value of the van drop below £15 000?
[2 marks]

....

(e) Sketch the graph to show the value of the van after t years.
[2 marks]

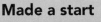 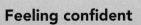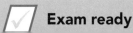

Ratio

② Quick quiz

Simplify each ratio.

(a) $2:8$ .... **(b)** $16:24$ .... **(c)** $4:\frac{3}{2}$ .... **(d)** $\frac{5}{2}:\frac{4}{3}$ ....

⑤ Ratios in context

Grade 5

1. Jim is building a house. He is putting some bricks and some blocks on a pallet.
The total number of bricks is 5 times the number of blocks.
The total number of bricks and blocks is 48. Each brick weighs 1.65 kg.
The total weight of the bricks and blocks is 76 kg. The blocks all weigh the same.
Work out the weight of one block. **[4 marks]**

> Number of bricks : number of blocks = 5 : ....
> Total number of parts = 5 + ...
>   = ... parts
> So .... parts = 48
> Number of bricks = 48 × .... ÷ .... = ...
> Number of blocks = 48 × .... ÷ .... = ...
> Total weight of bricks = ... × 1.65 kg
> Total weight of blocks = ...
> Weight of one block = ...

> Write down the ratio of the number of bricks to the number of blocks.

> Work out the number of bricks and the number of blocks.

> **Exam focus** 📌
> Make sure the units for bricks and blocks are the same.

.... kg

⑮ Using different types of ratio

Grade 5

2. The perimeter of a triangle is 255 cm. The lengths of the sides of the triangle are in the ratio $2:7:8$.
Work out the length of the longest side of the triangle. **[3 marks]**

3. At a hospital, the ratio of the number of men to the number of women is $2:3$.

30% of the men and 40% of the women are pensioners.

What percentage of all the people in the hospital are pensioners? **[4 marks]**

.... cm

.... %

4. A cubic metre of concrete has a mass of 2500 kg. Concrete is made from water, cement, sand and gravel. 12% of the concrete is water. The masses of the cement, sand and gravel are in the ratio $1:3:7$.

(a) Work out the masses of cement, sand and gravel in 1 cubic metre of concrete. **[4 marks]**

> You need to subtract the amount of water from the weight of the concrete.

....

Simon needs to make 44 cubic metres of concrete. He has 25 tonnes of gravel.

(b) Does Simon have enough gravel to make 44 cubic metres of concrete? You **must** show all of your working. **[3 marks]**

> As well as showing all of your working you need to answer yes or no.

....

✓ **Made a start**   ✓ **Feeling confident**   ✓ **Exam ready**

Proportion

Quick quiz

(a) If 10 sweets cost 30p, how much do 16 sweets cost?

....

(b) If 15 pens cost £3, how much do 8 pens cost?

....

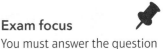

Currency conversions
Grade 5

1. The table shows the cost of a computer in three different countries.

	UK	Italy	USA
Price	£1520	€1770	$1925

The exchange rates are £1 = €1.25 and £1 = $1.32.
In which country would you pay the lowest amount for this computer?
You **must** show your working **[3 marks]**

 Italy = 1770 ÷ .... = £..............

USA = 1925 .... = £..............

....

Exam focus
You must answer the question fully, showing all your working.

Convert each currency into pounds so you can make a comparison.

To convert euros into pounds, divide by 1.25.

Indirect proportion
Grade 5

2. A publishing company employs a team of typists.
They know that 8 typists each working 6 hours a day can type a manuscript of a book in 20 days.
The publisher needs to type the manuscript of a book with the same number of pages within 14 days.
The team is increased to 15 typists each working 5 hours a day to complete the book.
Will they type the manuscript of this book within 14 days? You **must** show your working. **[4 marks]**

....

Direct proportion
Grade 5

3. Here are the ingredients needed to make 8 shortbread biscuits:
120 g butter, 60 g caster sugar, 180 g flour.
Mark has 660 g butter, 410 g caster sugar, 895 g flour.
Work out the greatest number of shortbread biscuits that Mark can make with his ingredients. You **must** show your working.

Work out the number of biscuits that can be made for each ingredient.

[3 marks]

....

Compound measures

② Quick quiz

1. Complete the sentence.

A compound measure is a mathematical measurement made up of .... or more other measures.

2. Tick (✓) the measures that are compound measures.

☐ speed ☐ length ☐ density ☐ area ☐ volume

⑤ Using the formula for pressure ⬛ Grade 6

1. A parcel exerts a force of 150 newtons on a table.
The pressure on the table is 40 N/m².
Work out the area of the box that is in contact with the table. **[3 marks]**

Rearrange the formula to find *A*.

$$40 = \frac{150}{A}$$

$A = ...$

$p = \dfrac{F}{A}$ where p = pressure, F = force, A = area

Exam focus 📌
You can leave your answer as a fraction or a decimal.

.... m²

⑩ Rates of change ⬛ Grade 6

2. The diagram shows a water container in the shape of a prism.
Ravi fills the container completely.
Water leaks from the bottom of the container at a constant rate.
The level of water falls by 15 cm in 1 hour and 30 minutes.
Water continues to leak from the trough at the same rate.
How many more minutes and seconds will it take for the container
to empty completely?

Split the shape into two cuboids.

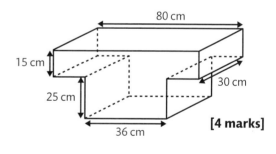

[4 marks]

.... minutes and .... seconds

⑤ Comparing rates of pay ⬛ Grade 6

3. Alan, Beth and Carina work for the same company. They receive their January payslips as shown below.

Alan	**Beth**	**Carina**
Net pay £1260	Net pay £1540	Net pay £950
160 hours worked	185 hours worked	110 hours worked

Whose rate of pay is the greatest? You **must** show your working. **[3 marks]**

....

☐ **Made a start** ☐ **Feeling confident** ☐ **Exam ready**

Speed

② Quick quiz

1. Distance = 30 miles, time = 3 hours

Work out the speed in miles per hour.

.... mph

2. Speed = 40 m/s, time = 12 s

Work out the distance in metres.

.... m

3. Distance = 500 km, speed = 75 km/h

Work out the time in hours.

.... hours

⑳ Speed in context   Grades 5–6

1. Ian travels from Penn to Malvern at an average speed of 40 mph.
He then travels from Malvern to Rye at an average speed of 60 mph.
Ian takes a total time of 4.5 hours to travel from Penn to Malvern.
The distance from Malvern to Rye is 180 miles.
Work out Ian's average speed for the total distance travelled from Penn to Rye.   **[4 marks]**

Penn to Malvern: $s = \dfrac{d}{t}$ so $40 = \dfrac{d}{4.5}$

$d = 4.5 \times 40 = $ .... miles

Malvern to Rye:

$s = \dfrac{d}{t}$ so $60 = \dfrac{180}{t}$

$t = \dfrac{180}{60} = $ .... hours

Total distance = ... + ...

= .... miles

Total time = ... + ...

= .... hours

.... mph

> Before you start, write down the formula for speed, distance and time.

> Work out the distance from Penn to Malvern.

> Work out the time taken from Malvern to Rye.

> **Exam focus** 📌
> To work out the average speed, you will need the total time taken and the total distance travelled.

2. Amina drives from Wolverhampton to Edinburgh. She drives at an average speed of 60 mph for the first 2 hours of her journey. She drives the remaining 160 miles at an average speed of 40 mph.
Amina thinks her average speed from Wolverhampton to Edinburgh is 50 mph.
Is she correct?
Tick a box.

Yes ☐   No ☐

Give a reason for your answer.   **[4 marks]**

....

3. The distance from Birmingham to Wolverhampton is 15 miles. The distance from Wolverhampton to Shrewsbury is 30 miles.
Tom lives in Birmingham. He is going to drive from his home to Wolverhampton, then from Wolverhampton to Shrewsbury for a meeting at 14:15.
Tom leaves Birmingham at 13:00. He drives from Birmingham to Wolverhampton at an average speed of 45 mph. He stops in Wolverhampton for 12 minutes. He drives from Wolverhampton to Shrewsbury at an average speed of 40 mph.
Will Tom arrive in Shrewsbury by 14:15? You **must** show your working.   **[4 marks]**

....

4. Connor finds information about two motorbikes.
Motorbike A has a maximum speed of 170 mph.
Motorbike B can travel 1 km in 15 seconds.
Which motorbike, A or B, is faster?
Use 5 miles = 8 km.   **[5 marks]**

....

Density

② Quick quiz

Complete these formulae.

(a) density = ...   **(b)** mass = ...   **(c)** volume = ...

 ⑩ Using density   Grade 5

1. Given that mass = 156 kg and volume = 30 m³, work out the density in kilograms per cubic metre. **[2 marks]**

> Write down the formula and then substitute the numbers.

$$d = \frac{m}{v}$$

$$= \frac{156}{\square}$$

.... kg/m³

2. Given that mass = 16 kg and density = 2.8 kg/m³, work out the volume in cubic metres. **[2 marks]**

> Substitute the numbers into the formula and then rearrange for volume.

$$2.8 = \frac{16}{v}$$

.... m³

3. Given that volume = 56 cm³ and density = 2.8 g/cm³, work out the mass in grams. **[2 marks]**

.... g

 ⑤ Combining densities   Grade 5

4. Asha mixes 190 g of metal A and 140 g of metal B to make an alloy. Metal A has a density of 18.2 g/cm³. Metal B has a density of 7.8 g/cm³. Work out the density of the alloy. **[4 marks]**

> **Exam focus** 📌
> To work out the density, you need the total mass and the total volume.

.... g/cm³

 ⑩ Application of the density formula   Grades 6–7

5. A frustum is made by removing a small cone from a large cone, as shown in the diagram.
The frustum is made from gold. Its mass is 15.6 kg.
Work out the density, in g/cm³, of the gold frustum.
Give your answer to 3 significant figures.

> The volume of a cone is $\frac{1}{3}\pi r^2 h$, where r is the base radius and h is the vertical height.

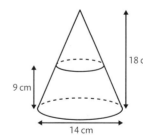

18 cm

9 cm

14 cm

> Work out the volume of the small and large cones.
>
> **[5 marks]**

.... g/cm³

6. The density of oak is 720 kg/m³. Tom is exporting oak to India.
A rectangular piece of oak measures 140 cm by 90 cm by 20 cm.
The maximum weight a pallet can hold is 2000 kg.
Work out the maximum number of pieces of oak the pallet can hold. You **must** show your working. **[4 marks]**

> Work out the volume of the cuboid.

....

Proportion and graphs

3.14

② Quick quiz

Choose one of these graphs to complete each sentence below.

A   **B**   **C**   **D**

(a) Graph .... represents direct proportion.   **(b)** Graph .... represents inverse proportion.

⑤ Setting up proportionality expressions — Grade 6

1. Y is directly proportional to X.
$Y = 48$ when $X = 5$.
Work out the value of Y when $X = 7$. **[2 marks]**

> Express the information as a ratio or an equation.

$$Y : 7 = 48 : 5$$

$$\frac{Y}{7} = \frac{48}{5}$$

> Solve the equation for Y.

....

> **Exam focus**
> Write out your equation clearly, using appropriate letters.

⑩ Using graphs — Grade 6

2. You can use this conversion graph to change between miles and kilometres.
Troy drove 210 kilometres in one week. Adam drove 138 miles in one week.
Troy claims that he drove further than Adam.
Is he correct? Tick a box. **[3 marks]**

Yes ☐   No ☐

Give a reason for your answer.

> When you are comparing distances, they must both be in the same units, for example, miles or kilometres.

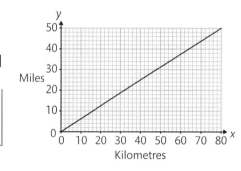

....

3. The diagram shows a straight line with equation $y = kx$ intersecting a curve with equation $y = \dfrac{4}{x}$ at the point $P(a, b)$.

(a) Work out a and b.
Give each answer in its simplest form, in terms of k. **[2 marks]**

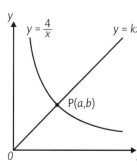

....

(b) Given that $a = 3b$, work out the value of k. **[2 marks]**

$$k = \dots\dots$$

Proportionality formulae

3 Quick quiz

$xy = k$ where k is a constant. Circle the correct statement.

y is directly proportional to x.   y is inversely proportional to x.

y is directly proportional to k.   y is inversely proportional to k.

---

5 Setting up a direct proportion equation   Grade 7

1. y is directly proportional to x.

When $x = 450$, $y = 12.5$.

(a) Write a formula for y in terms of x.   **[3 marks]**

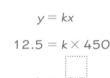
$y \propto x$

$y = kx$

$12.5 = k \times 450$

$k = \dfrac{\square}{\square}$

> Write down an expression in terms of y and x with the correct proportionality sign.

> Substitute the numbers into the expression and then rearrange and solve for k.

> **Exam focus** 📌
> Always work out the value of k and substitute it into the equation.

....

(b) Work out the value of y when $x = 720$.   **[1 mark]**

$y = \text{..........} \times \text{..........}$

....

---

10 Setting up proportion equations   Grade 7

2. y is inversely proportional to x. When $x = 9$, $y = 24$.
Work out the value of y when $x = 6.5$. Give your answer to 3 significant figures.   **[3 marks]**

....

3. The time, T seconds, it takes a tea urn to boil some water is directly proportional to the mass, m kg, of water in the tea urn.
When $m = 2.4$, $T = 540$.
(a) Work out the value of T when $m = 3.6$.   **[3 marks]**

....

The time, T seconds, it takes a travel kettle to boil a constant mass of water is inversely proportional to the power, P watts, of the kettle. When $P = 1200$, $T = 30$.
(b) Work out the value of T when $P = 750$.   **[3 marks]**

....

☑ Made a start   ☑ Feeling confident   ☑ Exam ready

Harder relationships

Write each of these numbers as a mathematical expression.

(a) the square of a | **(b)** the cube of b | **(c)** the square root of c | **(d)** the cube root of d

.... | .... | .... | ....

20 Setting up proportion equations | Grade 8

1. y is directly proportional to x^3. When $x = 10$, $y = 750$.

(a) Write a formula for y in terms of x.   **[3 marks]**

$y \propto x^3$

$y \ .... \ x^3$

$750 = ... \times 10^3$

$.......... = \dfrac{750}{\boxed{}}$

> Write an expression in terms of y and x^3 that includes a proportionality sign.

> Replace the proportionality sign with '$= k$'.

(b) Work out the value of x when $y = 384$.   **[2 marks]**

$y = ... \ x^3$

$384 = ... \ x^3$

$x^3 = \dfrac{384}{\boxed{}}$

$x = \sqrt[3]{\dfrac{384}{\boxed{}}}$

> **Exam focus**
> Work out the value of k and substitute it into the equation.

....

....

2. The pressure, P, at which petrol leaves a cylindrical pipe is inversely proportional to the square of the radius, r, of the pipe.
$P = 40$ when $r = 2.5$.

(a) Write a formula for P in terms of r.

> Use the inverse proportion rule.

[3 marks]

....

(b) Work out the value of P when $r = 1.25$.   **[1 mark]**

....

(c) Work out the value of r when $P = 10$.   **[1 mark]**

....

3. y is directly proportional to the square root of x. When $x = 36$, $y = 5$.

(a) Write a formula for y in terms of x.   **[3 marks]**

....

(b) Work out the value of x when $y = 7.5$.   **[2 marks]**

....

. y is inversely proportional to the square of x. Complete the table of values using this information.   **[4 marks]**

x	2	5	10	20
y				0.5

| ✓ **Made a start** | ✓ **Feeling confident** | ✓ **Exam ready** | 59 |

Ratio and proportion

 Ratio **Grade 6**

1. A mosaic is made from red shapes and green shapes.
Some of the shapes are circles and the rest of the shapes are squares.
The ratio of the number of red shapes to the number of green shapes is $3:7$.
The ratio of the number of red circles to the number of red squares is $4:5$.
The ratio of the number of green circles to the number of green squares is $2:5$.
Work out what fraction of all the shapes are squares. **[4 marks]**

Exam focus
Make sure you multiply and add the fractions correctly.

Write down the fraction of red shapes and of green shapes.

Work out the fraction of red squares and the fraction of green squares.

Add the two fractions together to work out the total fraction for squares.

....

 Proportion **Grade 8**

2. The table shows a set of values for x and y.

x	1	2	3	4
y	16	4	$\frac{16}{9}$	1

y is inversely proportional to the square of x.

(a) Write an equation for y in terms of x. **[2 marks]**

....

(b) Work out the positive value of x when $y = 25$. **[2 marks]**

....

(c) Sketch a graph that represents the relationship y is inversely proportional to the square of x. **[2 marks**

 Made a start **Feeling confident** **Exam ready**

Angle properties

⑤ Quick quiz

Tick (✓) the correct answers.

(a) Alternate angles are

☐ equal ☐ not equal.

(b) Corresponding angles are

☐ equal ☐ not equal.

(c) Vertically opposite angles are

☐ equal ☐ not equal.

(d) Allied angles add up to

☐ 180° ☐ 360°.

(e) Angles on a straight line add up to

☐ 180° ☐ 360°.

(f) Angles around a point add up to

☐ 180° ☐ 360°.

⑮ Using angle properties
Grades 5–6

1. *ABC* and *EDC* are straight lines.
AE and *BD* are parallel.
Angle *ABD* = 132°.
Angle *BCD* = 28°.

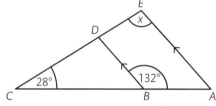

Work out the size of angle *DEA*, marked *x*. Give reasons for your answer. **[4 marks]**

Angle *CBD* = 180° − ....°

= ....° because angles on a straight line add up to ....°

Angle *CDB* = 180° − ....°

= ....° because angles in a .... add up to ....°

x = ...° because *x* and *CDB* are .... angles.

> Write down a reason to explain how you have worked out each angle.

> **Exam focus** 📌
> You must always give a reason for each step using correct mathematical language.

2. *ABC* and *DEF* are parallel lines.
BEG is a straight line.
Angle *GEF* = 44°.
Work out the size of the angle marked *x*.
Give reasons for your answer.

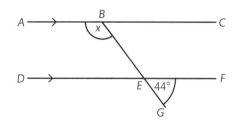

[3 marks]

....

....

3. *CDEF* is a straight line.
AB is parallel to *CF*.
DE = *AE*.
Work out the size of angle *ADC*, marked *x*.
Give reasons for your answer.

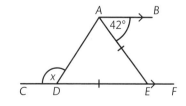

[4 marks]

....

....

Angle problems

⑤ Quick quiz

Look at the diagram and complete the sentences.

(a) Angle *d* and angle *f* are .... angles.

(b) Angle *c* and angle *g* are .... angles.

(c) Angle *e* and angle *g* are .... angles.

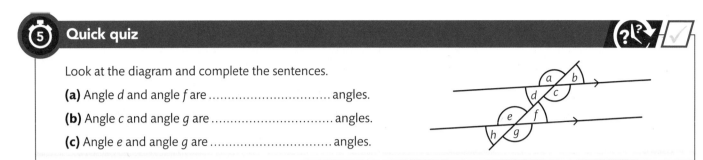

⑤ Application of angle properties   Grades 5–6

1. In the diagram, *ABC* and *EDC* are straight lines.
AE is parallel to *BD*.
Angle *EAC* = 39°.
Angle *ACE* = 33°.

Work out the size of angle *BDC*, marked *x*.
Give reasons for your answer.

[3 marks]

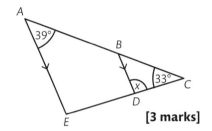

> Write the size of angle *DBC*.

> Refer to interior angles instead of Z angles and corresponding angles instead of F angles.

Angle *DBC* = ...° because it is a .... angle to

angle ....

x = ...° because angles in a .... add up to ....°.

Exam focus 📌
Give a reason for each step using correct mathematical language.

⑩ Application of angle properties   Grades 5–6

2. In the diagram, *LMN* is parallel to *PQR*.
QM = *QR*
Angle *RMN* = *x*°.
Angle *MQR* = *y*°.
Write down an expression for *y* in terms of *x*.

[2 marks]

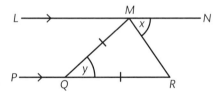

....

3. In the diagram, *PRS* and *TWY* are parallel straight lines.
QRWZ is a straight line.
Work out the value of *x*.
Give reasons for your answer.

[3 marks]

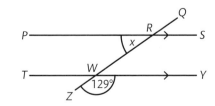

....

....

Angles in polygons

1. Complete the formulae.

(a) sum of exterior angles =

.... °

(b) exterior angle + interior angle =

.... °

2. Work out the

(a) exterior angle if the number of sides is 6

.... °

(b) number of sides if the exterior angle is 15°.

....

Regular polygons ⑤   **Grades 5–6**

1. The diagram shows part of a regular 12-sided polygon.
Work out the size of the angle marked *x*.   **[3 marks]**

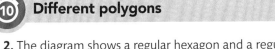

Exterior angle = ...

x = ...° − exterior angle

= ....° − ....°

Write down the formula for
the exterior angle.

Substitute 12 (the number
of sides) into the formula
to work out the exterior
angle.

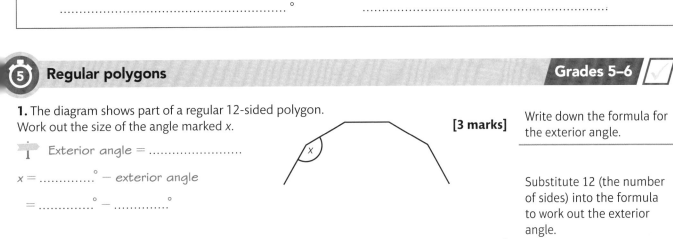

.... °

Different polygons ⑩   **Grades 5–6**

2. The diagram shows a regular hexagon and a regular octagon.
Work out the size of the angle marked *x*.
You **must** show your working.

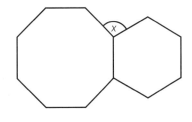

[4 marks]

.... °

3. The diagram shows a regular hexagon and a square.
Work out the value of the angle marked *x*.

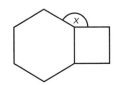

[4 marks]

.... °

4. The diagram shows a regular octagon.
Work out the size of the angle marked *x*.

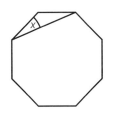

[4 marks]

.... °

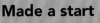

Constructing perpendiculars

 Quick quiz

Underline the correct answer.

(a) A bisector is a line that cuts another line in **half** / **thirds** / **quarters**.

(b) A perpendicular is a line that is at an angle of **180°** / **90°** to another line.

 Perpendicular bisector **Grade 5**

1. Construct the perpendicular bisector of the line *AB*. **[2 marks]**

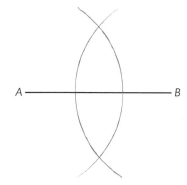

Make sure your compasses are set to a radius more than half of the length of the given line.

Place your compass point at *A* and draw an arc that crosses the given line. Do the same with the compass point at *B*.

Exam focus
Do not rub out your construction lines.

Join the two points where the arcs cross. This is the perpendicular bisector of *AB*.

 From a point to a line **Grade 5**

2. Construct the perpendicular from *P* to the line segment *AB*. **[2 marks]**

P
×

A ———————————————— B

 Point on a straight line **Grade 5**

3. Construct the perpendicular to the line segment *AB* at the point *P*. **[2 marks]**

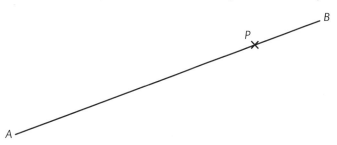

Constructions, plans and elevations

---

⑤ Quick quiz

Underline the correct answers.

(a) To construct a 60° angle, construct an **isosceles** / **equilateral** triangle.

(b) To construct a 45° angle, **dissect** / **bisect** a **60°** / **90°** angle.

(c) To construct a 30° angle, **dissect** / **bisect** a **60°** / **90°** angle.

---

⑤ Constructing an angle   Grade 5

1. Construct an angle of 60° in the space below.   **[2 marks]**

> Make sure the compasses are set to the length of the given line. Keep the compasses at this setting throughout the construction.

> Place your compass point at one end of the given line and draw an arc above the middle of the line. Do the same at the other end of the line.

Exam focus
Do not rub out your construction lines.

---

⑤ Drawing a prism   Grade 5

2. The plan, front elevation and side elevation of a solid prism are drawn on a centimetre grid.

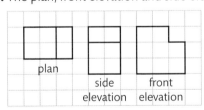

plan

side elevation   front elevation

Draw a sketch of the solid prism. Write the dimensions of the prism on your sketch.   **[2 marks]**

---

⑤ Bisecting an angle   Grade 5

3. Construct the bisector of angle *RPQ*.   **[2 marks]**

R

P   Q

Loci

⑤ Quick quiz

(a) Given that 1 cm represents 5 km, 6 cm represents

.... km.

(b) Given that 1 cm represents 50 m, 8 cm represents

.... m.

(c) Given that 1 cm represents 20 km, 50 km is represented

by .... cm.

⑤ Using scales   Grade 5

1. This is a map showing two points, X and Y, in Neil's garden.

> Set your compasses to the correct length, place the point at X and draw an arc.

X
×

Y
×

Scale: 1 cm represents 10 m.

Neil wants to plant a tree. The tree must be less than 20 m from X **and** less than 30 m from Y. Shade the region on the map in which Neil can plant the tree.   **[3 marks]**

⑤ Drawing loci   Grade 5

2. (a) Construct a locus of points that are the same distance from points A and B.   **[2 marks]**

(b) Construct a locus of points that are exactly 2 cm from line PQ.   **[2 marks]**

A
×

B
×

P ——————— Q

⑤ Using loci to solve problems   Grade 5

3. The diagram is a scale drawing of a rectangular garden ABCD.

Scale: 1 cm represents 1 metre.

Lisa wants to put a water fountain in her garden. It must be at least 3 m from point C, nearer to AB than to AD and less than 1.5 m from DC. On the diagram, shade the region where Lisa can put the water fountain.   **[4 marks]**

A

D

 Made a start   **Feeling confident**   ☑ **Exam ready**

Perimeter and area

② Quick quiz

Write down the formula for the area of

(a) a rectangle

(b) a triangle

(c) a circle.

....

....

....

⑳ Using algebra   **Grades 6–7**

1. The diagram shows a right-angled triangle and a rectangle.
The area of the triangle is twice the area of the rectangle.
Work out the perimeter of the rectangle.
You **must** show your working.

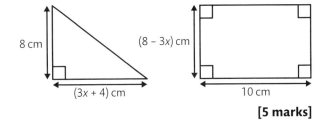

8 cm   (3x + 4) cm   (8 – 3x) cm   10 cm

Area of triangle $= \dfrac{1}{2} \times$ .... $\times$ .... $=$ ....

Area of rectangle $=$ .... $\times$ .... $=$ ....

[5 marks]

Area of triangle $= 2 \times$ area of rectangle

So .... $=$ ....

x $=$ ....

Work out the areas of the triangle
and the rectangle in terms of x.

Equate the areas by using the
condition given in the question.

.... cm

2. The diagram shows a circular pond, of radius r metres, surrounded
by a circular path.
The circular path has a constant width of 1 metre.
The area of the path is one-fifth of the area of the pond.

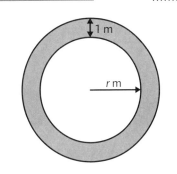

1 m   r m

(a) Show that $r^2 - 10r - 5 = 0$.   **[3 marks]**

(b) Work out the area of the pond. Give your answer to 3 significant figures.   **[3 marks]**

.... m²

3. The shape in the diagram is a compound shape. All the measurements are in centimetres.
All the corners are right angles. The area of the shape is 50 cm².
(a) Show that $4x^2 + 3x - 53 = 0$.   **[4 marks]**

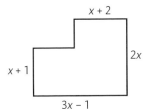

x + 2   2x   x + 1   3x – 1

(b) Work out the value of x. Give your answer to 3 significant figures.   **[2 marks]**

....

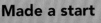

Volumes of 3D shapes

Write down the formula for the volume of

(a) a cone   **(b)** a sphere   **(c)** a square-based pyramid.

....

---

⑮ **Volumes of shapes**    **Grade 7**

1. The diagram shows a solid cylinder and a solid sphere.
   The cylinder has radius 4 cm and the sphere has radius 8 cm.
   The height of the cylinder is h cm.
   The total surface area of the sphere is twice the total surface area of the cylinder.
   Work out the volume of the cylinder.
   Give your answer to 3 significant figures.   **[5 marks]**

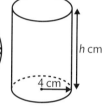

Total surface area = $2\pi rh + 2\pi r^2$
of the cylinder   = $2\pi(4)h + 2\pi(4)^2$
                   = $8\pi h + 32\pi$

Surface area = $4\pi r^2$
of the sphere = $4\pi(8)^2$
              = 256π

Work out the total surface areas
of the cylinder and the sphere.

$256\pi = 2 \times (8\pi h + 32\pi)$

.... = 16........ + ...

.... − .... = ... h

$h = $ ....

Use the condition in the
question to set up an equation.

.... cm³

2. A child's toy is made in the shape of a cone attached to a hemisphere. The volume
   of the cone is 540π cm³. The vertical height of the cone is 20 cm. Dan assumes that
   the diameter of the hemisphere is the same as the diameter of the base of the cone.

   (a) Use Dan's assumption to calculate the volume of the whole toy.   **[5 marks]**

20 cm

.... cm³

In fact, the diameter of the base of the cone is slightly smaller than the diameter of the hemisphere.

   (b) State whether the actual volume of the toy will be smaller or larger than your answer
       to part **(a)**.   **[1 mark]**

....

---

⑤ **Frustums**   **Grade 7**

3. A frustum is made by removing a small cone from a similar large cone.
   The height of the small cone is 20 cm. The height of the large cone is 40 cm.
   The diameter of the base of the large cone is 30 cm.
   Work out the volume of the frustum. Give your answer to 3 significant figures.   **[5 marks]**

20 cm

40 cm

30 cm

.... cm³

 Made a start   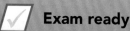 **Feeling confident**   **Exam ready**

Surface area

 Quick quiz

1. Write down a formula for the total surface area of

   (a) a cone   **(b)** a cylinder   **(c)** a sphere.

   ....

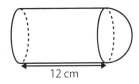 **Surface area of shapes**   **Grade 6**

1. The diagram shows a solid shape made from a cylinder and
   a hemisphere.
   The radius of the cylinder is equal to the radius of the hemisphere.
   The cylinder has a height of 12 cm.
   The area of the curved surface of the hemisphere is 72π cm^2.
   Work out the total surface area of the solid shape.
   Give your answer in terms of π.

   Work out the radius of
   the hemisphere.

   Work out the surface area
   of the cylinder.

   [5 marks]

 Area of curved surface of hemisphere $= 72\pi = \dfrac{1}{2} \times 4\pi r^2$

$4\pi r^2 = \ldots\ldots \times \ldots\ldots$

$r = \ldots\ldots$

Surface area of the cylinder $= \pi r^2 + 2\pi rh$

$\qquad\qquad = \ldots\ldots + \ldots\ldots$

Exam focus

Make sure you give the
answer in terms of π as
stated in the question.

Total surface area of solid shape $= \ldots\ldots + \ldots\ldots$

$\ldots\ldots\ldots\ldots\ldots\ldots$ cm^2

 Composite shapes   **Grade 6**

2. The diagram shows a solid made from a hemisphere and a cone.
   The radius of the hemisphere is 5 cm. The radius of the base of the cone is 5 cm.
   Work out the surface area of the solid. Give your answer to 3 significant figures.

   [5 marks]

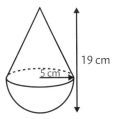

$\ldots\ldots\ldots\ldots\ldots\ldots$ cm^2

 Frustums   **Grade 6**

3. The slant height of the small cone is 20 cm. The slant height of the large cone is 40 cm.
   The diameter of the base of the large cone is 12 cm.
   Work out the total surface area of the frustum.
   Give your answer to 3 significant figures.

   [3 marks]

$\ldots\ldots\ldots\ldots\ldots\ldots$ cm^2

 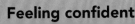

Prisms

 Quick quiz

Complete the sentences by crossing out the wrong answers.

(a) The cross-section of a prism is the **same / different** all along its length or height.

(b) The volume of a prism is its **cross-sectional area / length** × **volume / length**.

 Triangular prisms **Grade 5**

1. The diagram shows a triangular prism.

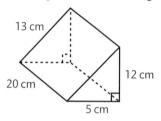

13 cm
20 cm
12 cm
5 cm

> Sketch all the sides of the shape first and find each individual area.

(a) Work out the total surface area of the prism. **[3 marks]**

 Area of triangular ends = 2 × .... × .... × .... = ...

Area of rectangular faces = ... × .... + ... × .... + ... × ....

> Add up all the areas to work out the total surface area.

.... cm²

(b) Work out the volume of the prism. **[2 marks]**

 Volume = cross-sectional area × length

Exam focus
You need to remember the formula
.... cm³   for the volume of a prism.

 Trapezoidal prisms **Grade 5**   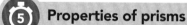 **Properties of prisms** **Grade 6**

2. The diagram shows a solid prism.

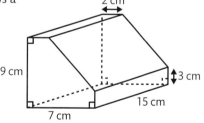

2 cm
9 cm
3 cm
15 cm
7 cm

3. A company transports boxes of wool in containers.
Each box is a cube of side 50 cm.
Each container is a cuboid measuring 4 m by 2.5 m by 2 m. The company has 830 boxes to transport and there are 4 containers.
Will the 830 boxes fit into these 4 containers?

[4 marks]

(a) Work out the volume of the prism. **[3 marks]**

.... cm³

(b) Work out the surface area of the prism. **[3 marks]**

....

.... cm²

 Made a start   **Feeling confident**   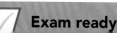 **Exam ready**

Circles and cylinders

⑤ Quick quiz

1. Write down the formula for

(a) the circumference of a circle

(b) the area of a circle

(c) the total surface area of a cylinder

(d) the volume of a cylinder.

....

2. A cylinder has a radius of 5 cm and a height of 14 cm. Work out

(a) its volume

(b) its total surface area.

.... cm³   .... cm²

⑤ Composite shapes   Grade 5

1. The diagram shows the path of an athlete on a running track.
The path consists of two straight lengths with a semicircle at each end.
Each straight length is 95 metres. Each semicircle has a radius of 33.5 metres.
Work out the area enclosed by the path.
Give your answer to 3 significant figures.

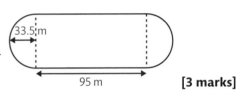

[3 marks]

Area of semicircular ends = πr² = ...

Area of rectangle = length × width = ...

> Consider the two semicircles as a circle.

> Work out the area of the rectangle.

Exam focus
Give your answer to the stated accuracy.

.... m²

⑤ Practical problems   Grade 5

2. A train has wheels of diameter 1.6 metres. The train travels 5 kilometres along a track.
Work out the number of complete turns made by one wheel of the train.

[4 marks]

....

⑤ Using exact values   Grade 7

3. The diagram shows a solid cylinder of radius $2\sqrt{5}$ cm and height h cm.
The total surface area of the cylinder is $60\pi\sqrt{15}$ cm².

Work out the exact value of h. Give your answer in the form $a\sqrt{3} + b\sqrt{5}$,
where a and b are integers. You **must** show your working.

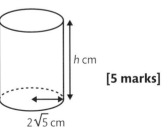

h cm

[5 marks]

$2\sqrt{5}$ cm

....

 Made a start   **Feeling confident**   **Exam ready**

Circles, sectors and arcs

② **Quick quiz**

Give a formula for

(a) the length of an arc of a circle .... **(b)** the area of a sector of a circle. ....

⑤ **Simple arcs and areas** **Grade 6**

1. A sector of a circle centre O has an angle of 50° and a radius of 7 cm. Work out

(a) the arc length **[1 mark]** **(b)** the area of the sector. **[1 mark]**

📍 Arc length $= 2\pi r \times \dfrac{\theta}{360}$ 📍 Area $= \pi r^2 \times \dfrac{\theta}{360}$

.... cm .... cm²

⑳ **Working out perimeters, arcs and areas** **Grade 6**

2. The diagram shows a flower bed in the shape of a sector of a circle.
Sandeep is going to put edging around the perimeter of the flower bed.
Edging is sold in lengths of 75 cm and each length of edging costs £1.89.
Work out the total cost of edging Sandeep needs to buy.

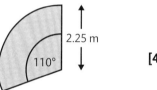
2.25 m
110° **[4 marks]**

📍 Arc length $= 2\pi r \times \dfrac{\theta}{360} =$ ....

Perimeter of flower bed = arc length + 2 × radius = ... + 2 ....

Number of lengths of edging required = ... ÷ .... = ...

> Remember to round up to find the total number of edging pieces.

📌 **Exam focus**
Make sure you give your final answer to 2 decimal places.

£...........................

3. The diagram shows a sector OAPB of a circle, centre O.
AB is a chord of the circle and OA = OB = 6.2 cm. Angle AOB = 78°.
Work out the area of the shaded segment APB.
Give your answer to 3 significant figures.

[5 marks]

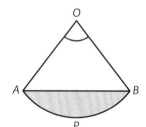
O
A B
P

.... cm²

4. OAB is a sector of a circle, centre O and OCD is another sector of the same circle, centre O.
OCA and ODB are straight lines. Angle AOB = 75°. OD = 8 cm and DB = 6 cm.
Giving your answers to 3 significant figures, work out

(a) the perimeter of the shaded region **[3 marks]**

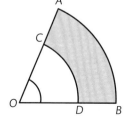
A
C
O D B

.... cm

(b) the area of the shaded region. **[3 marks]**

.... cm

✓ **Made a start** ✓ **Feeling confident** ✓ **Exam ready**

Circle facts

② Quick quiz

Complete the sentences by crossing out the incorrect words.

(a) A tangent is a **curved** / **straight** line that touches the circumference of the circle just once.

(b) A tangent is **parallel** / **perpendicular** to the radius at the point of contact.

(c) Two tangents intersecting at a point outside the circle are **equal** / **different** in length.

⑳ Using circle facts **Grade 6**

1. R and T are points on a circle, centre O.
ROP is a straight line.
PT is a tangent to the circle.
Angle TPO = 52°.
Work out the size of angle TRO.
You must give a reason for each stage of
your working.

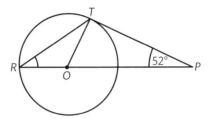

Exam focus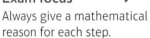
Always give a mathematical
reason for each step.

[4 marks]

Angle OTP = ... ° because ....

Angle POT = ... ° because ....

Angle ROT = ... ° because ....

Angle TRO = ... ° because ....

2. A and B are points on the circumference of a circle, centre O.
AC and BC are tangents to the circle.
Angle ACB = 48°.
Work out the size of angle OBA.
You must give a reason at each stage of your working.

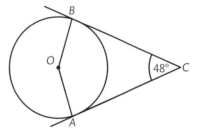

[4 marks]

....

....

3. A and B are points on the circumference of a circle, centre O.
AT is a tangent to the circle.
Angle TAB = 61°.
Angle BTA = 43°.
Work out the size of angle OBT.
You must give a reason for each stage of your working.

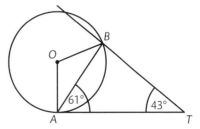

[5 marks]

....

....

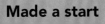

Circle theorems

② Quick quiz

Complete the sentences by choosing from the list below.

equal   equal to   not equal to   twice   90°   180°   360°

(a) The angle subtended at the centre is .... the angle subtended at the circumference.

(b) Angles in the same segment are ....

(c) The angle subtended by a diameter of a circle is always ....

(d) Opposite angles in a cyclic quadrilateral add up to ....

㉕ Working out the size of angles

Grade 8

1. A, B, C and D are four points on a circle, centre O.
AD is a diameter of the circle.
Angle BAD = 54°.

(a) Work out the size of angle ADB.

Give reasons for your answer.

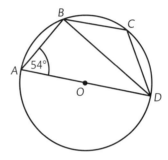

> Write down angles
> ABD and ADB, with
> reasons.

[2 marks]

Angle ABD = ... ° because it is subtended by ....

Angle ADB = ... ° because ....

(b) Work out the size of angle BCD.

Give a reason for your answer.   **[2 marks]**

Angle BCD = ... ° because ....

2. A, B and C are points on a circle, centre O.
Angle ACB = 79°
PA and PB are tangents to the circle.
Work out the size of angle APB.
You must give a reason at each stage of your working.

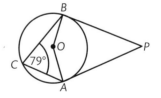

[4 marks]

....

....

3. A, B, C and D are points on a circle.
PDQ is a tangent to the circle at D.
Angle BDA = 26° and angle BCD = 78°.
Work out the size of angle ADP.
You must give a reason at each stage of your working.

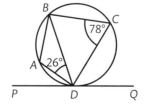

[3 marks]

....

....

 Made a start   **Feeling confident**   **Exam ready**

Transformations

Write down the names of the four transformations.

....

20 Application of transformations   **Grade 5**

1. (a) Rotate triangle A 90° clockwise about the point (0, 1).
Label the new triangle B.   **[2 marks]**

The points in a reflected image should be the same distance from the mirror line as the corresponding points in the object, but on the other side of the mirror line.

Trace shape A. Keep the paper in place by putting your pencil at (0, 1).

Rotate the tracing 90° clockwise to find the position of the image.

The top number gives the number of units moved on the x-axis. A negative number means a move to the left. The bottom number gives the number of units moved on the y-axis. A negative number means a move down.

(b) Reflect triangle A in the line $x = -1$. Label the new triangle C.   **[2 marks]**

(c) Translate triangle A by $\begin{pmatrix} -4 \\ -7 \end{pmatrix}$. Label the new triangle D.   **[2 marks]**

Exam focus
Always label your object and image shapes.

2. Describe fully the single transformation that maps

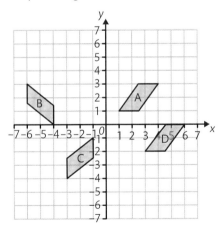

(a) shape A onto shape B   **[2 marks]**

....

(b) shape A onto shape C   **[2 marks]**

....

(c) shape A onto shape D.   **[2 marks]**

....

3. A sketch of a quadrilateral *ABCD* is shown.

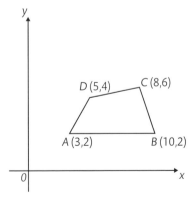

ABCD is enlarged, centre *C*, scale factor 2.

Circle the vertex that is invariant.   **[1 mark]**

A   *B*   *C*   *D*

Enlargement

Quick quiz

Complete each sentence by crossing out the incorrect word.

(a) A scale factor greater than 1 means that the image is **smaller** / **larger** than the object.

(b) A scale factor less than 1 means that the image is **smaller** / **larger** than the object.

(c) A negative scale factor means that the image and object are on the **same** / **opposite** sides of the centre of enlargement.

Negative scale factor Grade 6

1. On the grid, enlarge the shape by scale factor −0.5 with centre (0, 0). **[4 marks]**

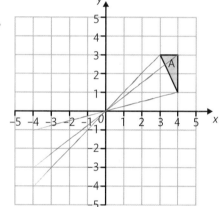

Draw a line from each vertex of shape A through the origin.

On each of these lines, measure how far the vertex is from the origin, then mark a point at half this distance on the other side of the origin.

Exam focus
Do not rub out your construction lines.

Join the three points you have marked to produce the image.

Describing an enlargement Grade 4   ## Enlargement on a grid Grade 4

2. Describe fully the single transformation that maps triangle A onto triangle B. **[3 marks]**

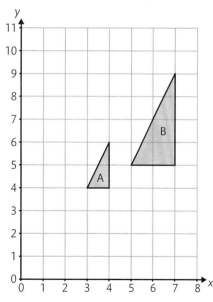

3. On the grid, enlarge the shape by scale factor 3 with centre A. **[3 marks]**

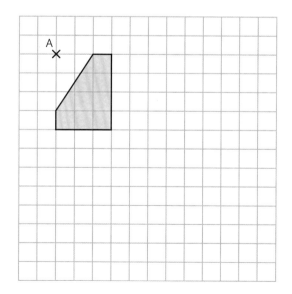

....

....

Made a start   Feeling confident   Exam ready

Combining transformations

5 Quick quiz

Complete each sentence by crossing out the incorrect word.

(a) After a reflection, the image is **congruent** / **similar** to the object.

(b) After a rotation, the image is **congruent** / **similar** to the object.

(c) After a translation, the image is **congruent** / **similar** to the object.

(d) After an enlargement, the image is **congruent** / **similar** to the object.

15 Describing single transformations   Grade 6

1. Shape P is reflected in the line $y = -1$ to give shape Q.
Shape Q is reflected in the line $x = 0$ to give shape R.
Describe fully the single transformation that maps shape P onto shape R.   **[3 marks]**

> Draw the line $y = -1$. Reflect shape P in it to produce shape Q.

> Draw the line $x = 0$. Reflect shape Q in it to produce shape R.

> A single transformation means just one reflection, rotation, translation or enlargement.

Exam focus
Use the correct mathematical language, including the name of the transformation, about a point, clockwise or anticlockwise and the number of degrees.

....

....

2. Shape Q is rotated 180° about the point $(0, -1)$ to give shape R. Shape R is reflected in the line $y = -1$ to give shape S. Describe fully the single transformation that maps shape Q onto shape S.   **[3 marks]**

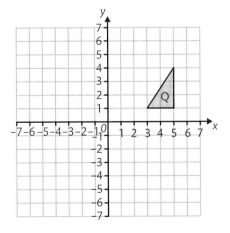

3. Triangle A is rotated 90° clockwise about the origin to give triangle B. Triangle B is translated by the vector $\binom{-4}{-2}$ to give triangle C. Describe fully the single transformation that maps triangle A onto triangle C.   **[3 marks]**

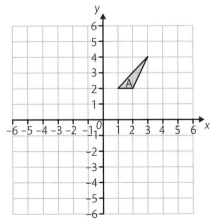

....

....

....

....

  Made a start   **Feeling confident**   **Exam ready**

3.14

BBC

Bearings

⑤ Quick quiz

Complete the sentences.

(a) Bearings are always measured from the .... line and given as .... digits.

(b) In the bearing of B from A, the angle is measured from point ....

(c) In the bearing of A from B, the angle is measured from point ....

⑮ Giving bearings Grade 5

1. The diagram shows the positions of a mountain *M*, a climber *C* and a beacon *B*.

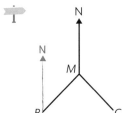

> Draw a north line at *B*.

> Use a protractor to measure the angles.

> You can use the rules for alternate or corresponding angles.

The bearing of *B* from *M* is 224°.

(a) Give the bearing of *M* from *B*. **[2 marks]**

📌 **Exam focus**
Always give bearings as three digits.

.................................°

The bearing of *C* from *M* is 112°.

(b) Give the size of angle *BMC*. **[1 mark]**

.................................°

(c) Given also that *BM* = *CM*, give the bearing of *C* from *B*. **[1 mark]**

.................................°

2. The diagram shows two points *S* and *T*.
The bearing of *T* from *S* is 053°.
Work out the bearing of *S* from *T*. **[2 marks]**

.................................°

3. The diagram shows the positions of three points, *A*, *B* and *C*, on a map.
The bearing of *B* from *A* is 072°.
Angle *ABC* is 48°.
AB = *CB*.
Work out the bearing of *C* from *A*. **[3 marks]**

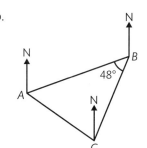

.................................°

Scale drawings and maps

③ Quick quiz

A scale of 1 cm represents 20 km.

(a) Give the actual distance represented by 4.5 cm.

.....................km

(b) Give the length that represents a distance of 65 km.

.....................cm

⑳ Distances and bearings   Grade 5

1. The diagram shows the positions of a lighthouse *L*, a buoy *B* and a ship *S* on a map.
Scale: 1 cm represents 20 km.

(a) Measure the bearing of *L* from *B*.   **[1 mark]**

> Draw a line from *L* to *B*.

> Use a protractor to measure the angle *NBL*.

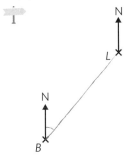

.................................°

The ship, *S*, sails 90 km on a bearing of 270°.

(b) Work out the distance, in kilometres, between the ship and the lighthouse when the ship is at its closest point to the lighthouse.   **[2 marks]**

> Use a protractor to construct the angle 270° to show the direction the ship now follows. Label this line *ST*.

Length *LR* = ... cm

Distance *LR* = ... × .... = ... km

.................................km

> Construct the perpendicular from *L* to the new line *ST*. Label the foot of the perpendicular *R*.

2. The diagram shows the positions of a lighthouse *L* and a port *P*.

Scale: 1 cm represents 10 km.

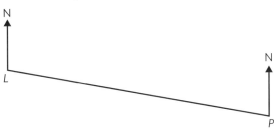

(a) Work out the real distance between *L* and *P*.   **[1 mark]**

.................................km

(b) Measure the bearing of *P* from *L*.   **[1 mark]**

.................................°

Ship *S* is 20 km from *L* on a bearing of 035°.

(c) On the diagram, mark the position of ship *S* with a cross (×). Label it *S*.   **[2 marks]**

 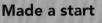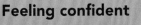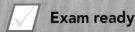

Similar shapes

Work out

(a) $\sqrt{\dfrac{64}{25}}$ ....

(b) $\sqrt[3]{\dfrac{125}{27}}$ ....

(c) $\left(\dfrac{5}{4}\right)^2$ ....

(d) $\left(\dfrac{3}{2}\right)^3$. ....

1. Two plant pots, A and B, are mathematically similar.
A has a height of 8 cm and B has a height of 12 cm. A has a surface area of 80 cm².

(a) Work out the surface area of B. **[2 marks]**

Length scale factor = $12 \div 8 = 1.5$

> Work out the scale factor
> for the length and square it
> to find the area scale factor.

.... cm²

(b) B has a volume of 405 cm³.
Work out the volume of A. **[2 marks]**

Volume of A = $405 \div 1.5^3$

> The volume scale factor will be the
> cube of the length scale factor.

.... cm³

2. Cuboid A and cuboid B are mathematically similar.
The ratio of the volume of cuboid A to the volume of cuboid B is 27 : 8.
The surface area of cuboid A is 432 cm².
Work out the surface area of cuboid B. **[3 marks]**

Volume scale factor = $\dfrac{8}{27}$

Length scale factor = $\sqrt[3]{\dfrac{8}{27}}$

> Wok out the scale factor for the
> volume and cube root it to find
> the length scale factor.

Exam focus
To find the area scale factor,
square the length scale factor.

.... cm²

3. The diagram shows two similar cones, A and B.

(a) Cone A has a volume of 80 cm³.
Work out the volume of cone B. **[2 marks]**

A
5 cm

B
10 cm

.... cm³

(b) Cone B has a surface area of 160 cm².
Work out the surface area of cone A. **[2 marks]**

.... cm²

4. Vases A and B are mathematically similar.
Vase A has a surface area of 120 cm². Vase B has a surface area of 750 cm² and a volume of 1600 cm³.
Work out the volume of vase A. **[3 marks]**

.... cm³

 Made a start **Feeling confident** **Exam ready**

Congruent triangles

---

(2) Quick quiz

What is the reason that these two triangles are congruent? Circle your answer.

         SAS   RHS   SSS   AAS

---

(5) Proving triangles are congruent   **Grade 6**

1. Show that triangle *ABC* is congruent to triangle *EFD*.   **[3 marks]**

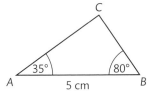 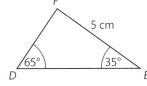

Angle ACB = 180 − (35 + 80) = 180 − 115 = 65°

Angle DFE = 180 − (35 + 65) = ...

> If you know two angles in a triangle, you can work out the third angle.

> Knowing that both triangles contain the same three angles does not necessarily show congruence.

Exam focus

Make sure you write which condition you have used to show congruence (SAS, RHS, SSS, AAS, ASA)

---

(10) Triangles in composite shapes   **Grade 5**

2. Shape *ABCD* is a rhombus. *M* is the midpoint of line *BD*. Prove that triangle *DMC* is congruent to triangle *BMC*.
   [3 marks]

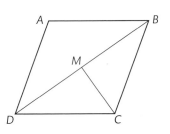

3. *ABCD* is a kite. Show that triangle *ABC* is congruent to triangle *ADC*.
   [3 marks]

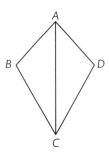

Pythagoras' theorem

⏱ 5 · Quick quiz

1. Give a mathematical statement for Pythagoras' theorem. ....

2. Work out the unknown sides of the triangles. All lengths are in centimetres. Leave your answers as surds.

(a)

(b)

(c)

.... cm   .... cm   .... cm

⏱ 15 · Using Pythagoras' theorem   Grades 5–7

1. The diagram shows a quadrilateral *ABCD*.
$AB = 50$ cm and $AD = 14$ cm.
$BD : BC$ is in the ratio $2 : 3$.
Angle ADB = angle $CBD = 90°$.
Work out the length of *CD*.
Give your answer to 3 significant figures.

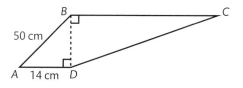

[4 marks]

 $50^2 = 14^2 + BD^2$

$2500 = 196 + BD^2$

$BD^2 = 2500 - ....$

$BD = ...$

$BD : BC = 2 : 3$, so $BC = ... \times ....$

In triangle *BDC*, applying Pythagoras' theorem gives ....

So $CD^2 = ...$

.... cm

Exam focus
Show each step of your working.

Work out the length of *BD* by applying Pythagoras' theorem to triangle *ABD*.

Write down and apply Pythagoras' theorem in triangle *BCD*.

2. The diagram shows a rectangular framework.
The framework is made from 5 wooden rods.
The wooden rods weigh 0.25 kg per metre.
Work out the total weight of the framework.
Give your answer in kilograms to 3 significant figures.

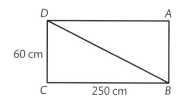

[4 marks]

.... kg

3. The diagram shows a triangle *EFB* inside a rectangle *ABCD*.
Work out the area of triangle *EFB*.
You **must** show your working.

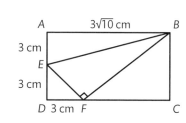

[4 marks]

.... cm²

 Made a start   Feeling confident   Exam ready

Pythagoras' theorem in 3D

⑤ Quick quiz

Work out the unknown side in each triangle.

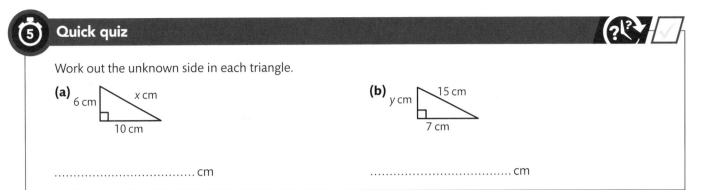

(a) 6 cm, x cm, 10 cm

(b) y cm, 15 cm, 7 cm

.... cm   .... cm

⑮ 3D problems   Grade 7

1. In the diagram, *ABCDEFGH* is a cuboid.
AB = 6 cm, *BF* = 7 cm and *AD* = 15 cm.
Work out the length *AG*.
Give your answer to 3 significant figures.

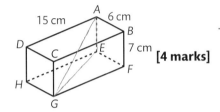

$GE^2 = 6^2 + 15^2$

$GE^2 = 36 + 225$

6 cm, 15 cm

$GE^2 = ...$

In triangle AGE: $AG^2 = ... + ...$

$AG = ...$

Draw a line from *A* to *G*.

For each stage, draw a right-angled triangle to help you see which length you are working out.

Never round your answers in your working as you will lose accuracy on the final answer.

[4 marks]

.... cm

2. The diagram shows a triangular prism with cross-section *PQR*.
MR = 85 cm, *MP* = 84 cm and *PQ* = 12 cm. Angle *PQR* = 90°.
Work out the length *RL*.
Give your answer to 1 decimal place.

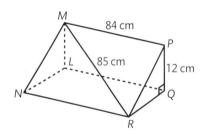

[4 marks]

.... cm

3. The diagram shows a wooden frame, *VABCD*, in the shape of a right pyramid on a square base. The wooden frame is made from 8 lengths of wood.
V is vertically above the centre of the square.
OV = 2.5 m and *AD* = 5 m.
A length of 1 metre of the wood costs £1.45. Gary has £60.
Does Gary have enough money to buy the wood for the frame?
You **must** show your working.

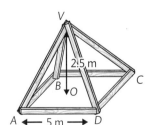

[5 marks]

....

Units of length, area and volume

---

② Quick quiz

Complete the conversions.

(a) 1 cm = ... mm   **(b)** 1 m = ... cm   **(c)** 1 m = ... mm   **(d)** 1 km = ... m

---

⑤ Simple conversions   **Grade 5**

1. (a) Circle the area that is the same as 48 mm².   **[1 mark]**

| 480 cm² | 4800 cm² | 0.48 cm² | 4.8 cm² |

> Scale factor for area is the scale factor for length, squared.

(b) A rectangle has an area of 452 000 cm². Write this area in m².   **[2 marks]**

452 000 cm² = ... ÷ (.........) m²

.... m²

Exam focus

Remember your metric conversions.

2. The volume of a metal ball is 3375 mm³. A number of these metal balls are melted to make a cuboid. The volume of the cuboid is 648 cm³. Work out the number of balls that are melted down to make the cuboid.   **[2 marks]**

....

---

⑤ Using distances   **Grade 5**

3. Mark is on holiday in France.
He is driving to Paris on the motorway.
Mark drives past this road sign.
Mark stops at a service station 35 miles after he sees the road sign.
Work out how far Mark still has to drive from the service station to get to Paris.
Give your answer in kilometres.
5 miles ≈ 8 km.

Paris   283 km

[3 marks]

.... km

---

⑤ Using volumes   **Grade 5**

4. The diagram shows a water butt used to store rainwater.
The container is in the shape of a cylinder of radius 50 cm.
The height of the rainwater in the water butt is 95 cm.
70 litres of rainwater are taken from the container.
Work out the new height of the rainwater in the water butt.
Give your answer to 1 decimal place.
1 litre = 1000 cm³.

95 cm

50 cm

[4 marks]

.... cm

 Made a start   **Feeling confident**   **Exam ready**

Trigonometry: lengths

② Quick quiz

Write each of these ratios in terms of the opposite, adjacent and hypotenuse.

(a) $\sin \theta = $ ………

(b) $\cos \theta = $ ………

(c) $\tan \theta = $ ………

---

⑤ Simple trigonometry
Grade 4

1. The diagram shows a right-angled triangle.
Work out the value of x.
Give your answer to 3 significant figures. **[2 marks]**

> Label the sides as hyp, opp and adj.

adj = 21.6 and hyp = x

SOH (CAH) TOA

> Write down SOH CAH TOA.

………63° = ⬚/⬚

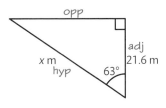

> Choose the correct trigonometrical ratio.

....

2. Work out the missing length in each of these triangles.

(a) x **[2 marks]**

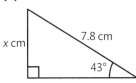

....

(b) PR **[2 marks]**

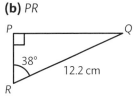

.... cm

---

⑩ Using trigonometry
Grade 5

3. In the diagram, PSR is a straight line.
Angle $PSQ = 90°$, $PS = 9.2$ cm.
Angle $QPS = 42°$, angle $SQR = 46°$.
Work out the length of QR.
Give your answer to 3 significant figures. **[4 marks]**

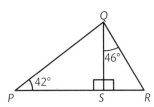

.... cm

4. Donna works out the length AB to 3 significant figures.
She writes:

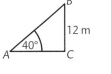

$$\sin x = \frac{\text{opp}}{\text{hyp}}$$

$$\sin 40° = \frac{AB}{12}$$

$$AB = 12 \times \sin 40°$$

$$AB = 7.713 \text{ m}$$

Comment on Donna's method and answer. **[2 marks]**

....

....

Trigonometry: angles

 2 **Quick quiz**

Work out the size of these angles.

(a) $\tan \theta = 3.45$, $\theta = $ ....$^\circ$ **(b)** $\sin \theta = 0.78$, $\theta = $ ....$^\circ$ **(c)** $\cos \theta = 0.34$, $\theta = $ ....$^\circ$

 5 **Simple trigonometry**   **Grade 5**

1. Circle the exact value of $\sin 60°$.   **[1 mark]**

$\dfrac{3}{\sqrt{2}}$ $\dfrac{\sqrt{3}}{2}$ $\dfrac{\sqrt{2}}{2}$ $\dfrac{2}{\sqrt{2}}$

> Label the sides hyp, opp and adj.

2. Work out the value of x.
Give your answer to 1 decimal place.   **[2 marks]**

> Write down SOH CAH TOA.

 adj = 28.5 and opp = 19.4

SOH CAH (TOA)

.... $x = \dfrac{\Box}{\Box}$

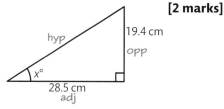

> Choose the correct trigonometrical ratio.

..................................$^\circ$

 15 **Using trigonometry**   **Grade 5**

3. The diagram shows triangle ABC.
D is the point on AB such that CD is perpendicular to AB.
$AC = 9.4$ cm, $AD = 5.2$ cm and $BD = 7.8$ cm.
Work out the size of angle ABC.
Give your answer to 1 decimal place.

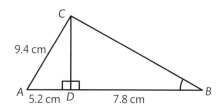

[4 marks]

..................................$^\circ$

4. In the diagram, ABC is a right-angled triangle.
D is a point on AB.
Angle $ACD = 35°$.
$AD = 11.3$ cm, $DB = 6.5$ cm and $AC = 19.6$ cm.
Work out the size of the angle labelled x.
Give your answer to 1 decimal place.

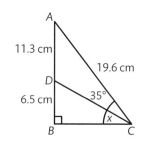

[4 marks]

..................................$^\circ$

 Made a start   **Feeling confident**   **Exam ready**

Trigonometry techniques

---

② Quick quiz

Write down the exact values for

(a) $\tan 60°$ ....

(b) $\sin 45°$ ....

(c) $\cos 30°$ ....

---

⑤ Working out angles   **Grades 5–6**

1. Work out the size of angle x in each diagram.

Label the sides hyp, opp and adj.

(a)

hyp, x, $30\sqrt{3}$ cm, adj, opp, 30 cm

(b)

$2\sqrt{3}$ cm, x, 2 cm

(c)

6 cm, x, $6\sqrt{2}$ cm

🪧 SOH CAH TOA

.............................° ....° ....°

---

⑩ Real-life problems   **Grades 5–6**

2. The diagram shows a ladder leaning against a vertical wall.
The ladder stands on horizontal ground.
The length of the ladder is 6 m.
The bottom of the ladder is 3 m from the bottom of the wall.
A ladder is safe to use when the angle marked x is exactly 65°.
Is the ladder safe to use?
You **must** show your working.

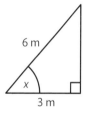
6 m, x, 3 m

[3 marks]

You need to be able to answer a question like this without using a calculator.
You need to know that $\cos 60° = \frac{1}{2}$.

....

3. The diagram shows a tower.
The point A is at the top of the tower.
The point B is at the foot of the tower.
There is a balcony at the point D on the tower.
B and C are points on horizontal ground.
$BD = 20$ m.
The angle of elevation of A from C is 60°.
The angle of elevation of D from C is 30°.
Work out the exact height, AB, of the tower.

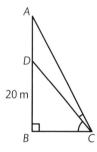
A, D, 20 m, B, C

[5 marks]

.... m

Trigonometry in 3D

Quick quiz

Work out the unknown values.

(a) $\tan 35° = \dfrac{x}{24}$ ....

(b) $\sin 42° = \dfrac{38}{y}$ ....

(c) $\cos 50° = \dfrac{19.4}{z}$ ....

Cuboids

Grade 6

1. The diagram shows a cuboid *ABCDEFGH*.
$AB = 10$ cm, $AF = 8$ cm and $BC = 4\sqrt{14}$ cm.
(a) Work out the length of *FC*.
Give your answer to
3 significant figures.

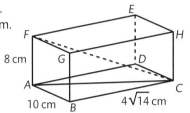

[3 marks]

Draw right-angled triangles at each stage.

_____

Label the sides hyp, opp, adj.

$$10^2 + (4\sqrt{14})^2 = AC^2$$

$AC = $ ....

Exam focus 📌

Give your answer to the required degree of accuracy.

.... cm

(b) Work out the size of the angle between the line *FC* and the plane *ABCD*.
Give your answer to 1 decimal place.

[2 mark

....

Cubes

Grade 6

2. The diagram shows a cube *ABCDEFGH*.
The lengths of the sides of the cube are 12 cm.
Work out the size of the angle between the diagonal *AH*
and the base *EFGH*.
Give your answer to 1 decimal place.

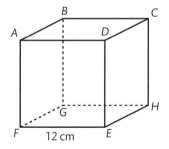

[4 mark

....

Pyramids

Grade 6

3. The diagram shows a pyramid with a horizontal rectangular base *PQRS*.
$PQ = 18$ cm and $QR = 12$ cm. *M* is the midpoint of the line *PR*.
The vertex, *T*, is vertically above *M*. $MT = 16$ cm.
Work out the size of the angle between *TP* and the base *PQRS*.
Give your answer to 1 decimal place.

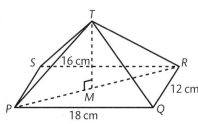

[4 mark

....

Made a start ✓   **Feeling confident** ✓   **Exam ready** ✓

The sine rule

② Quick quiz

Write down the version of the sine rule you would use to find

(a) the length of a side   ....   **(b)** an angle.   ....

⑮ Using the sine rule   **Grade 7**

1. The diagram shows triangle *ABC*.
Giving your answers to 3 significant figures, work out

> Write down the version of the sine rule to use.

(a) the size of angle *BAC*   **[3 marks]**

> Substitute known values.

$$\frac{\sin A}{BC} = \frac{\sin B}{AC}$$

$$\frac{\sin A}{13.4} = \frac{\sin 124}{16.8}$$

> Rearrange.

$$\sin A = \text{.........}$$

$$A = \text{.........}°$$

...................................°

(b) the length of *AB*.   **[2 marks]**

$$\frac{AB}{\sin C} = \frac{AC}{\sin B}$$

> Write down the version of the sine rule to use.

$$\frac{AB}{\sin\text{........}} = \frac{16.8}{\sin 124}$$

> Substitute known values. Use your value for *A* to work out *C*.

$$AB = \frac{16.8\ \sin\text{........}}{\sin 124}$$

.... cm

Triangle diagram (question 1): *A*, 16.8 cm, *C*, 124°, 13.4 cm, *B*

2. The diagram shows triangle *PQR*.
Work out the length of *PR*.
Give your answer to 3 significant figures.

12.5 cm   135°   **[3 marks]**

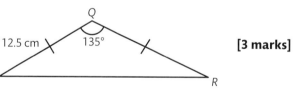

P   *Q*   *R*

.... cm

. *NQ* is a straight line.
Point *P* is on line *NQ*.
Line *PT* = 3.2 km.
Work out the length of *QT*.
Give your answer to 3 significant figures.

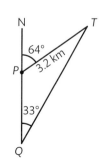

N   *T*   64°   3.2 km   *P*   33°   *Q*

[3 marks]

.... km

The cosine rule

② Quick quiz

Write down the version of the cosine rule you would use to find

(a) the length of a side .... **(b)** an angle. ....

⑮ Using the cosine rule

Grade 7

1. In the diagram, $AB = 12.9$ cm and $BC = 25.4$ cm.
Angle $ABC = 72°$.
Work out the length of AC.
Give your answer to 3 significant figures.

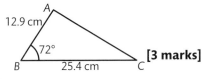

[3 marks]

$$AC^2 = AB^2 + BC^2 - 2 \times AB \times BC \times \cos B$$

$$AC^2 = 12.9^2 + 25.4^2 - (2 \times 12.9 \times 25.4 \times \cos 72°)$$

You can only use the cosine rule when the angle is between the two given sides.

Write out the cosine rule.

Substitute what you know.

Exam focus 📌

Show the substitution of numbers into the cosine rule clearly.

.... cm

2. The diagram shows triangle ABC.
$AB = 4.1$ cm, $AC = 5.4$ cm and $BC = 7.6$ cm.
Work out the size of the largest angle.
Give your answer to 3 significant figures.

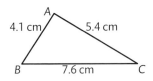

The largest angle is always opposite the longest side.

[3 marks]

....

3. In the diagram, $AC = (2x + 1)$ cm, $BC = (x + 2)$ cm and $AB = (x + 1)$ cm.
Angle $ABC = 60°$.
Work out the value of x.

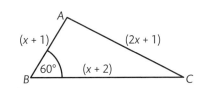

[5 marks]

....

☑ **Made a start** ☑ **Feeling confident** ☑ **Exam ready**

Triangles and segments

5

Quick quiz

Work out

(a) the area of the triangle

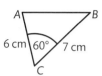

6 cm 60° 7 cm
A   B
C

.... cm²

(b) the length of the arc

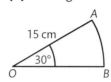

15 cm
30°
O   B
A

.... cm

(c) the area of the sector.

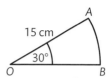

15 cm
30°
O   B
A

.... cm²

Areas   Grade 7

1. The diagram shows triangle *ABC*.
$AB = 12.9$ cm and $BC = 25.4$ cm.
Angle $ABC = 72°$.
Work out the area of triangle *ABC*.
Give your answer to 3 significant figures.

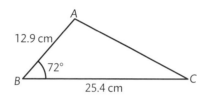

12.9 cm
72°
B   25.4 cm   C
A

> You can only use the formula for the area of a triangle when the angle is between the two given sides.

[3 marks]

Area of triangle $= \dfrac{1}{2}ab \sin C$

$= \dfrac{1}{2} \times \text{...............} \times \text{...............} \times \sin 72°$

.... cm²

Exam focus

Show the substitution of numbers into the area of a triangle formula clearly.

2. The diagram shows a circle, centre *C*. *AB* is a chord of the circle.
The area of the shaded region is 200 cm².
Angle $ACB = 30°$.
Work out the length of the radius.
Give your answer to 3 significant figures.

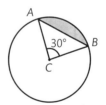

A
30° B
C

[4 marks]

.... cm

3. The shape in the diagram is made from triangle *ABC* and a sector of a circle, centre *C* and radius *CA*.
$CA = 8$ cm, $CB = 20$ cm and angle $ACB = 120°$.
Work out the area of the shape.
Give your answer to 3 significant figures.

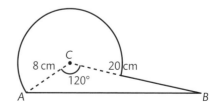

C
8 cm   20 cm
120°
A   B

[4 marks]

.... cm²

Vectors

⑤ Quick quiz

Complete the sentences.

(a) Vectors are quantities that have both .... and ....

(b) $\begin{pmatrix} x \\ y \end{pmatrix}$ is called a .... vector. The top number gives the ....

The bottom number gives the ....

⑤ Column vectors   **Grade 7**

1. $\mathbf{a} = \begin{pmatrix} -5 \\ 3 \end{pmatrix}$ and $\mathbf{b} = \begin{pmatrix} -9 \\ -4 \end{pmatrix}$.

Circle the vector $\mathbf{a} - \mathbf{b}$.

$\begin{pmatrix} -14 \\ -1 \end{pmatrix}$ $\begin{pmatrix} 4 \\ 7 \end{pmatrix}$ $\begin{pmatrix} -4 \\ -7 \end{pmatrix}$ $\begin{pmatrix} 14 \\ 1 \end{pmatrix}$

[1 mark]

2. In the diagram, ABCD is a parallelogram.

$\overrightarrow{BA} = \begin{pmatrix} -2 \\ -6 \end{pmatrix}$ and $\overrightarrow{DA} = \begin{pmatrix} -8 \\ -2 \end{pmatrix}$.

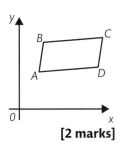

Work out $\overrightarrow{DB}$ and write it as a column vector.   **[2 marks]**

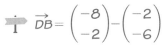 $\overrightarrow{DB} = \begin{pmatrix} -8 \\ -2 \end{pmatrix} - \begin{pmatrix} -2 \\ -6 \end{pmatrix}$

Exam focus
Column vectors can be added and subtracted.

....

⑩ Working out and using vectors   **Grade 7**

3. The diagram shows a trapezium PQRS.
$\overrightarrow{PQ} = \mathbf{a}$ and $\overrightarrow{QR} = \mathbf{b}$.
PS is parallel to QR. PS = 5QR.
Work out, in terms of $\mathbf{a}$ and/or $\mathbf{b}$

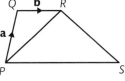

(a) $\overrightarrow{PS}$ **[1 mark]**

....

(b) $\overrightarrow{PR}$ **[1 mark]**

....

(c) $\overrightarrow{RS}$.   **[1 mark]**

....

4. The diagram shows a parallelogram, ABCD.
M is the midpoint of AD.
$\overrightarrow{AM} = \mathbf{a}$ and $\overrightarrow{AB} = \mathbf{b}$
Work out, in terms of $\mathbf{a}$ and/or $\mathbf{b}$

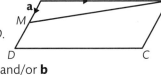

(a) $\overrightarrow{AD}$ **[1 mark]**

....

(b) $\overrightarrow{AC}$ **[1 mark]**

....

(c) $\overrightarrow{MB}$.   **[1 mark]**

....

 Made a start   **Feeling confident**   **Exam ready**

Vector proof

② Quick quiz

Complete the sentences.

(a) Two vectors are equal if they have the same .... and ....

(b) Two vectors are parallel if they are in the same ....

⑮ Proof using vectors   Grade 7

1. ABC is a triangle. D is the point on BC such that $BD:DC = 7:5$.
$\vec{AB} = 4\mathbf{a}$ and $\vec{AC} = 4\mathbf{b}$.

Show that $\vec{AD} = k(5\mathbf{a} + 7\mathbf{b})$, where k is a scalar quantity to be found.   **[4 marks]**

Work out $\vec{BC}$, $\vec{BD}$ and then $\vec{AD}$.

$\vec{BC} = -4a + 4b$

$\vec{BD} = \dfrac{7}{12}\vec{BC}$

$\vec{AD} = \vec{AB} + \vec{BD}$

$\phantom{\vec{AD}} = \text{...............} + \text{...............}$

$k = \text{...............}$

If $\vec{AB}$ represents $4\mathbf{a}$ then $\vec{BA}$ represents $-4\mathbf{a}$.

Vectors can be added and subtracted using the rules of algebra.

$\vec{BD}$ can be written as $\dfrac{7}{12}\vec{BC}$.

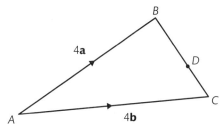

2. $ABCD$ is a parallelogram.
G is the midpoint of DC and F is the midpoint of AG.
$\vec{DG} = \mathbf{a}$ and $\vec{AD} = 3\mathbf{b}$.
$DE:EA = 2:1$.
Prove that EFC is a straight line.   **[5 marks]**

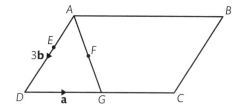

. ABC is a triangle. D is the point on BC such that $BD:DC = 3:2$.
$\vec{AB} = 7\mathbf{a}$ and $\vec{AC} = 3\mathbf{b}$.

Show that $\vec{AD}$ is parallel to $(14\mathbf{a} + 9\mathbf{b})$.   **[4 marks]**

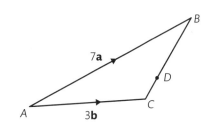

Line segments

Complete the sentences.

(a) .... theorem can be used to work out the distance between two points.

(b) Write down the formula to work out the midpoint of two points (x_1, y_1) and (x_2, y_2): ....

⑤ **Line segments on graphs**   **Grade 7**

1. In the diagram, the straight line L passes through the points A and B.

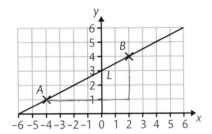

> To find the midpoint, add the x-values and divide by 2, then do the same for the y-values.

(a) Work out the coordinates of the midpoint of AB.   **[2 marks]**

$$\frac{-4 + 2}{2} = \text{...............} \quad \text{and} \quad \frac{\text{...........} + \text{...........}}{2} = \text{...............}$$

....

(b) Work out the distance AB. Give your answer in the form $a\sqrt{5}$ where a is an integer.   **[3 marks]**

> Draw a triangle to help you work out the length of AB.

$$AB^2 = (\text{........} - \text{........})^2 + (\text{........} - \text{........})^2$$

$$= \text{...............} + \text{...............}$$

> Use Pythagoras' theorem to work out the length of AB.

....

⑩ **Working out distances**   **Grade 7**

2. The straight line L passes through the points $P(7, 4)$ and $Q(11, 10)$.

    (a) Write down the coordinates of the midpoint of PQ.   **[2 marks**

....

    (b) Work out the distance PQ. Give your answer in the form $a\sqrt{13}$ where a is an integer.   **[3 marks**

....

3. The point M has coordinates $(-4, 1)$. The point N has coordinates $(3, 6)$.

    (a) Write down the coordinates of the midpoint of MN.   **[2 marks]**

    (b) Work out the distance MN. Give your answer to 3 significant figures.   **[3 mark**

....

Geometry and measures

Working out vectors   Grade 7

1. $\mathbf{a} = \begin{pmatrix} -4 \\ -1 \end{pmatrix}$ and $\mathbf{b} = \begin{pmatrix} 3 \\ -1 \end{pmatrix}$. James works out $2\mathbf{a} + 3\mathbf{b}$. His answer is $\begin{pmatrix} 1 \\ -5 \end{pmatrix}$.

Is James correct?

Tick a box.

Yes ☐   No ☐

Give a reason for your answer.   **[2 marks]**

....

....

Circle theorems   Grade 7

2. In the diagram, B, C and D are points on the circumference of a circle, centre O.
BOD is a diameter of the circle.

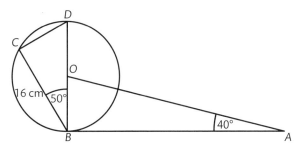

Exam focus
Draw a diagram for each stage of the calculation to help you visualise what you are working out.

Write down the size of angle BCD.

Work out the length of BD and then length BO.

AB is a tangent to the circle at B. BC = 16 cm. Angle CBD = 50°. Angle BAO = 40°.
Work out the length of OA. Give your answer to 3 significant figures.   **[5 marks]**

.... cm

Pythagoras' theorem   Grade 7

3. In the diagram, ABCDEF is a triangular prism.
AB = 10 cm, BC = 18 cm and AE = 15 cm.
Angle ABC = 90°.
M is the midpoint of CD.

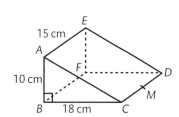

Work out the size of the angle between AM and the plane BCDF.
Give your answer to 1 decimal place.   **[5 marks]**

.... °

Probability

A number is chosen at random from the following list: 5 7 8 2 4 3

Give the probability that the number chosen is

(a) even .... **(b)** prime .... **(c)** a square number. ....

⑤ Using tables Grade 5

1. Jordan plays a game in which he throws a hoop at a target.
The table shows information about the probability of each possible score.

Score	0	1	2	3	4
Probability	x	$2x$	0.20	0.12	0.23

> The probabilities of all possible outcomes total 1.

(a) Work out the value of x. **[3 marks]**

 $x + 2x + 0.20 + 0.12 + 0.23 =$ ....

.... $x =$ ....

> Set up an equation in x and then solve it.

....

Jordan plays the game twice.

(b) Work out the probability of Jordan scoring a total of 6. **[3 marks]**

$6 =$ .... + ... or .... + ... or .... + ...

$p(6) =$ .... + ... + ...

> Write down all the ways of getting a total of 6.

> **Exam focus** 📌
> Give probabilities as decimals or fractions.

....

⑮ Working out probabilities Grade 5

2. The probability that a lorry will pass an emissions test is 0.90. Three lorries are tested.

(a) Work out the probability that none of these lorries will pass the emissions test. **[2 marks]**

....

(b) Work out the probability that exactly one of these lorries will pass the test.
You **must** show your working. **[3 marks]**

3. Peter throws a fair dice twice.

(a) Work out the probability that he gets the number 4 both times. **[2 marks]**

....

(b) Emma keeps rolling this dice until she rolls a 4. Work out the probability that Emma rolls the dice

(i) exactly twice **[2 marks]**

....

(ii) more than three times. **[2 marks]**

....

 Made a start **Feeling confident** **Exam ready**

Relative frequency

 Quick quiz

A coin is tossed 20 times and a head is obtained 8 times.
Write down the relative frequency for the number of heads. ....

 Probability and relative frequency | **Grade 5**

1. A box contains 30 plastic plates. The table shows information about the radii of the plates.

Radius of plastic plate (cm)	3	4	5	6	7
Frequency	4	7	6	8	5

> **Exam focus**
> Give your answers as fractions or decimals.

A plate is taken at random from the box. Work out the probability that the radius of the plate is

(a) 3 cm　　　　**[1 mark]**　　**(b)** not 5 cm　　　　**[2 marks]**　　**(c)** more than 5.5 cm.　**[2 marks]**

Probability = $\dfrac{\square}{30}$　　　　Probability = $\dfrac{\square}{30}$　　　　Probability = $\dfrac{\square}{30}$

....　　　　........................　　　　........................

2. There are 80 tiles in a bag. There are five different colours of tile. The table shows information about the tiles in the bag.

Colour of tile	Red	Yellow	Blue	Green	Black
Frequency	14	17	23	16	10

A tile is taken at random from the bag. Work out the probability that the tile is

(a) yellow or blue　　　　　　**[2 marks]**　　**(b)** not black.　　　　　　**[2 marks]**

....　　　　　　　　........................

Sandra takes a tile at random from the bag. She records the colour of the tile and then replaces the tile in the bag.
Anjali then takes a tile from the bag at random.

(c) Work out the probability that Sandra takes a red tile and Anjali takes a green tile.　　**[3 marks]**

....

3. Jake rolls a biased dice 60 times and records five 6s.

Sarah rolls the same dice 300 times and records thirty 6s.

(a) Whose results will give the best estimate for the probability of the dice landing on a 6?
Give a reason for your answer.　　　　**[2 marks]**

....

Amir rolls the same dice two more times.

(b) Combine Jake and Sarah's results to estimate the probability that Amir scores a 6 on his first roll and a different number on his second roll.　　　　**[2 marks]**

....

Venn diagrams

Tick (✓) the correct box. The area of a Venn diagram where two loops overlap represents

☐ outcomes that can never occur together   ☐ outcomes that can occur together.

㉕ **Using Venn diagrams**   **Grade 8**

1. In Year 11, there are 60 students. 20 of the students study textiles, 15 of the students study food science and 9 of the students study both.

(a) Show this information on a Venn diagram.

textiles — food science — 9

> Students who study both subjects are represented in the overlap.

One of the 60 students is chosen at random. Work out the probability that the student

(b) does not study textiles and does not study food science   **[2 marks]**

....

(c) studies textiles or studies food science, but not both.   **[2 marks]**

....

> To work out the number of students who study only textiles or only food science, subtract 9 from the total number of students who study each subject.

> To find the number of students who study neither subject, add together the numbers in the three parts of the Venn diagram and subtract the result from 60.

2. When 100 people were surveyed about the types of exercise they did, it was found that:
64 jog, 55 row, 56 cycle, 38 jog and row, 32 row and cycle, 36 jog and cycle and 20 do all three.

(a) Draw a Venn diagram to represent this information.   **[4 marks]**

(b) Work out the probability that a person selected randomly from the survey

(i) takes none of these types of exercise   **[2 marks]**

....

(ii) only rows or only jogs or only cycles.   **[2 marks]**

....

3. (a) Which of these represents the shaded region? Circle your answer.   **[1 mark]**

$(A \cap B)'$ $A' \cap B$

$A \cap B'$ $A \cup B$

(b) Which of these represents the shaded region? Circle your answer.   **[1 mark]**

$A \cup B'$ $A' \cup B'$

$A' \cup B$ $A \cap B$

☐ **Made a start**   ☐ **Feeling confident**   ☐ **Exam ready**

Conditional probability

② Quick quiz

Complete the sentence by crossing out the incorrect words.

Conditional probability is the probability of an event occurring given that another event **has** / **has not** occurred.

⑤ Using two-way tables

Grade 9

1. 50 children were asked which of three genres of film they liked the best.
   The two-way table shows the results of the survey.

	Action films	Animated films	Musicals	Total
Boys	10	14	7	
Girls	6	4	9	
Total				

Exam focus 📌
Answers can be left as fractions.

One of the children is picked at random.

(a) Write down the probability that this child will be

Work out how many girls there are in the sample.

   (i) a girl **[1 mark]**

   $$\text{Probability} = \frac{6 + \ldots + \ldots}{50}$$

   ....

   (ii) a boy who liked action films the best. **[2 marks]**

   $$\text{Probability} = \frac{\square}{50}$$

   ....

(b) A girl is chosen at random. What is the probability that she likes animated films the best? **[2 marks]**

....

⑤ Using Venn diagrams

Grade 9

2. $\mathscr{E} = \{\text{customers at a restaurant}\}$
   $S = \{\text{customers who had starters with their meal}\}$
   $D = \{\text{customers who had desserts with their meal}\}$

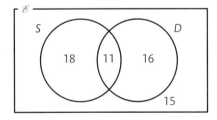

A customer is chosen at random.

(a) Work out the probability that the customer had both a starter and a dessert with their meal. **[2 marks]**

....

(b) Work out the probability that the customer had a starter given that the customer also had a dessert. **[2 marks]**

....

Conditional probability

Grade 9

3. Edgar has some sweets. He has 10 strawberry sweets, 7 mint sweets and 8 raspberry sweets.
   Edgar is going to choose 2 sweets at random.
   Work out the probability that the 2 sweets will not both be the same flavour.
   You **must** show your working. **[4 marks]**

....

 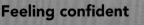

Tree diagrams

---

② Quick quiz

Tick (✓) the correct box.

Probabilities can be represented on a ☐ box plot ☐ tree diagram ☐ sample space diagram.

㉕ Drawing tree diagrams

Grades 5–7

1. Andrea has two bags. In bag A, there are 6 black counters and 4 green counters.
In bag B, there are 4 black counters and 3 green counters.
Andrea is going to take at random one counter from bag A and one counter from bag B.

(a) Complete this tree diagram to show this information. **[3 marks]**

$\frac{6}{10}$ — black

$\frac{4}{10}$ — green

> The tree diagram starts with two branches for bag A, then each branch is extended for bag B.

(b) Work out the probability that both counters will be black. **[2 marks]**

Probability $= \dfrac{\Box}{10} \times \dfrac{\Box}{7} = \dfrac{\Box}{\Box}$

....

> **Exam focus** 📌
> You multiply along the branches.

(c) Work out the probability that exactly one of the counters will be black. **[3 marks]**

Probability $= \left(\dfrac{\Box}{10} \times \dfrac{\Box}{7} \right) + \left(\dfrac{\Box}{10} \times \dfrac{\Box}{7} \right) = \dfrac{\Box}{\Box}$

....

> Write down the probabilities for the black counter from bag A and the black counter from bag B.

2. There are 9 chocolate cookies and 6 oatmeal cookies in a tin. Kamila takes a cookie from the tin at random and eats it. Then Henry takes a cookie from the tin at random and eats it.

(a) Show this information on a tree diagram. **[3 marks]**

(b) Work out the probability that both cookies will be chocolate. **[2 marks]**

....

(c) Work out the probability that either Kamila will eat an oatmeal cookie and Henry won't, or Henry will eat an oatmeal cookie, but Kamila won't. **[3 marks]**

....

3. Mahad either cycles to school or goes by bus. On any day that he goes to school, the probability that he cycles is 0.65. When he cycles, the probability that he is late is 0.15. When he goes by bus, the probability that he is late is 0.25.

(a) Show this information on a tree diagram. **[3 marks]**

(b) Work out the probability that on a day Mahad goes to school, he cycles and is late for school. **[2 marks**

....

  Made a start **Feeling confident** **Exam ready**

Probability

 Probability

1. There are 11 counters in a bag. 8 of the counters are red.
3 of the counters are yellow.
Sofiyaan takes two counters from the bag at random.
Showing your working, work out the probability that Sofiyaan takes one counter of each colour

> 'With replacement' means the counter is put back into the bag.

(a) with replacement **[3 marks]**

> 'Without replacement' means the counter is not put back into the bag.

....

Exam focus 📌

For without replacement probabilities, the total number and number available both get one smaller each time.

(b) without replacement. **[4 marks]**

....

 Venn diagrams

2. 90 people were asked which sport they liked the most. Their replies showed that:
32 liked football (F), 34 liked cricket (C), 39 liked tennis (T), 12 liked football and tennis,
13 liked football and cricket, 11 liked cricket and tennis, 7 liked football, cricket and tennis.

(a) Complete the Venn diagram to show this information. **[4 marks]**

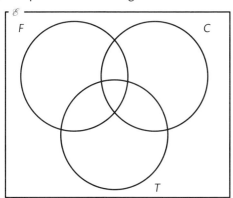

(b) Work out the probability that a person chosen at random likes exactly one of these sports. **[2 marks]**

....

(c) Given that a person chosen at random liked tennis, work out the probability that this person also liked football.
[2 marks]

....

Sampling

② Quick quiz

Tick (✓) the correct box. A sample is random when

☐ all the individuals in the population have an equal chance of being chosen.

☐ the population is divided into strata and then each person has an equal chance of being chosen from the strata.

⑤ Data collection

Grade 5

1. Keith wants to find out the types of film people like best. He is going to ask whether they prefer thriller films, horror films, science fiction films or musicals.

(a) Design a suitable table for a data collection sheet he could use to collect this information. **[2 marks]**

🪧	Thriller	Horror		
Tally				

> Draw a table and write down the headings.

Exam focus 📌
Give clear and concise answers.

Keith collects his data by asking 10 people in his office at work.
This might not be a good way to find out the types of film people like best.

(b) Give **two** reasons why. **[2 marks]**

1. ....

2. ....

⑮ Samples and surveys

Grade 5

2. A company makes 2000 bolts. Tara is going to take a random sample of 20 of these bolts.
Describe a method she could use to select the sample. **[2 marks]**

....

....

3. Len is doing a survey to find out how many magazines people buy.
He chooses his friends at school to fill out his survey.
This may not be a good sample to use. Give **two** reasons why. **[2 marks]**

1. ....

2. ....

4. Govind is doing a survey to find out how often people travel by train. He is going to ask 10 people as they are leaving a railway station. Give **two** reasons why this may not be a good sample for Govind's survey. **[2 marks]**

1. ....

2. ....

☑ Made a start ☑ Feeling confident ☑ Exam ready

Mean, median and mode

 Quick quiz

1. Write down what you understand by

   (a) the mode   **(b)** the median   **(c)** the mean.

....

2. The mean length of 10 pieces of fabric is 147 cm. Work out the total length of the fabric.

.... cm

 **Working out a combined mean**   **Grade 5**

1. 55 adults sat an aptitude test. 15 men sat the test and they had a mean score of 102.
40 women sat the test and they had a mean score of 108.
Work out the mean score of all 55 adults.   **[3 marks]**

> Work out the total score for the men and the total score for the women.

$$\text{Mean} = \frac{\text{total of all data values}}{\text{number of data values}}$$

Exam focus
A common error is to add up the mean scores and divide by 2.

> Add up the total scores and divide by the total number of men and women.

$$\text{Mean} = \frac{(15 \times 102) + (\dots \times \dots)}{55}$$

....

 Using mean, mode and median   **Grade 5**

2. Sarah has five cards. She wants to write down a number on each card such that the mode of the five numbers is 14, the median is 17, the mean is 18 and the range is 12. Work out the five numbers she writes on the cards.

            [3 marks]

Using the combined mean   **Grade 5**

3. The times that Ada, Bill, Charlie and Dan took to run a race were recorded. The mean of these times was 13.5 seconds. Ed also ran the race. The combined mean time for all five people was 14 seconds.
Work out the time it took Ed to run the race. **[3 marks]**

.... s

 Working out the mean from frequency tables   **Grade 5**

4. In 2016, Natalie recorded the midday temperature in her garden for each day in April, May and June.
She used the information to produce this table.

	April	May	June
Mean midday temperature (°C)	6.5	11.3	13.9
Number of days	30	31	30

Work out the mean midday temperature for this period. Give your answer to 1 decimal place.   **[3 marks]**

.... °C

Frequency tables

(5) Quick quiz

Look at this set of data: 3   3   5   5   5   5   8   8   8   9   10   12   14   15   16

Write down

(a) the mode ....   **(b)** the median ....   **(c)** the mean ....

(5) Averages from a frequency table

Grade 5

1. The table gives information about the numbers of medals gained by the younger boys at a running club.

Number of medals	Frequency	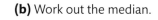 fx
0	19	
1	16	
2	9	
3	7	
4	4	

> Add another column to work out fx.

> The mode is the number that occurs most often. It has the highest frequency.

> The median is the middle number in the ordered data.

(a) Write down the mode.

[1 mark]

> **Exam focus**
> Do not mix up the three different averages.

....

(b) Work out the median.

[1 mark]

Total = 19 + 16 + 9 + 7 + 4 = ...

Median = $\frac{1}{2}$ (........)th value = ...

....

(c) Work out the mean number of medals.

[2 marks]

Mean = $\frac{\text{total of all data values}}{\text{number of data values}} = \frac{\sum fx}{\sum f}$ $\sum fx$ = ...

$\sum f$ = ...

....

(10) Averages from a grouped frequency table

Grades 5–6

2. David asked some people how many minutes they each took to get to work. The table shows some information about his results.

Number of minutes, t	Frequency, f
$0 \leq t < 10$	7
$10 \leq t < 20$	11
$20 \leq t < 30$	16
$30 \leq t < 40$	19
$40 \leq t < 50$	12

(a) Work out the class interval that includes the median.

[1 mark]

.... minutes

(b) Work out an estimate for the mean time taken.

[3 marks]

.... minutes

(c) Explain why your answer to part **(b)** is an estimate.

[1 mark]

....

....

 Made a start   **Feeling confident**   **Exam ready**

Interquartile range

② Quick quiz

Work out the difference between the 4th and 12th values in this data set.

3   3   5   5   5   5   8   8   8   9   10   12   14   15   16

....

⑤ Interquartile range from discrete data

Grade 6

1. These are the ages of 15 people who attend a yoga class:

55   44   16   17   43   24   21   19   37   33   46   15   46   21   46

Work out the interquartile range.   **[2 marks]**

> Use the formula
>
> $Q_3 = \frac{3}{4}(n+1)$th term.

15   16   17   19   ....

UQ = ...

LQ = ...

IQR = UQ − LQ

> Use the formula
>
> $Q_1 = \frac{1}{4}(n+1)$th term.

....

⑤ Using interquartile range to find other measures

Grade 6

2. The table gives information about the weights of some parcels, in kilograms.

Least weight	Greatest weight	Range	Lower quartile	Upper quartile	Interquartile range
	29.8 kg	23.2 kg	15.8 kg		7.2 kg

Complete the table.   **[2 marks]**

⑩ Interquartile range from stem-and-leaf diagrams

Grade 6

3. Peter plays 15 games of ten-pin bowling. Here are his scores:

61   48   64   55   68   64   55   52

78   65   54   68   66   60   72

(a) Draw an ordered stem-and-leaf diagram to show Peter's scores.   **[2 marks]**

(b) Work out the range.   **[1 mark]**

....

(c) Work out the interquartile range.   **[2 marks]**

....

Line graphs

⑤ Quick quiz

Look at this set of data: 14   18   16   12   13   19   24   36   36

Write down

(a) the mode   **(b)** the median   **(c)** the mean.

....

⑩ Interpreting line graphs   Grade 5

1. Shauna asked some people how many driving tests they had each taken. The table gives information about her results.

Number of driving tests	1	2	3	4	5
Frequency	11	9	6	4	3

Exam focus
Make sure you know the difference between the mean, mode and median.

(a) Complete the bar-line graph for the information in the table.   **[2 marks]**

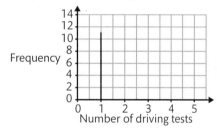

(b) Write down the mode.   **[1 mark]**

The mode is represented by the tallest line.

....

(c) Work out the mean number of driving tests.   **[3 marks]**

Mean = [(1 × 11) + (2 × ....) + (3 × ....) + (4 × ....) + (5 × ....)] ÷ 33

To find the mean, find the total number of tests and divide the answer by the total number of people taking the tests.

....

⑤ Interpreting time series graphs   Grade 5

2. The time series graph gives some information about the number of televisions sold in a shop in each quarter of 2010 and 2011.

(a) Work out the total number of televisions sold in quarter 1 of 2010 and quarter 1 of 2011.   **[2 marks]**

....

(b) Describe the trend in the number of televisions sold in the shop from 2010 to 2011.   **[1 mark]**

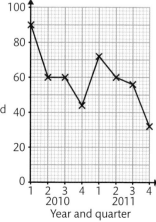

....

✓ **Made a start**   ✓ **Feeling confident**   ✓ **Exam ready**

Scatter graphs

② Quick quiz

Write down the type of correlation shown when data on a scatter graph is going

(a) upwards from left to right .... **(b)** downwards from left to right. ....

---

⑩ Interpreting scatter graphs **Grades 5–6**

1. Ryan recorded the heights in centimetres and the weights in kilograms of 9 different students. The scatter graph shows information about his results.
One of the points is an outlier.

> An outlier is a point that does not follow the trend of the data.

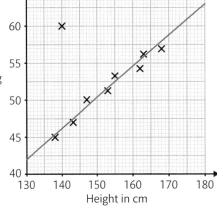

Weight in kg

Height in cm

(a) Write down the coordinates of the outlier. **[1 mark]**

....

(b) For all the other points

(i) draw the line of best fit **[1 mark]**

(ii) describe the correlation. **[2 marks]**

....

> 'Describe the correlation' means say whether it is positive or negative.

A student is 180 cm tall.

(c) Estimate the weight of this student. **[1 mark]**

.... kg

(d) Is this estimate reliable? Give a reason for your answer. **[1 mark]**

....

 Drawing scatter graphs **Grades 5–6**

2. The table shows information about 8 apartments in a city. The table shows the distance, in miles, from the city centre and the monthly rent, in pounds, of each apartment.

Distance from city centre	3.4	1.4	0.6	2.4	1.8	0.9	4.1	3.2
Monthly rent (£)	130	330	510	280	400	440	120	140

(a) Draw a scatter graph for the information in the table. **[3 marks]**

(b) Describe and interpret the correlation. **[3 marks]**

....

....

An apartment is 2.8 miles from the city centre.

(c) Estimate the monthly rent for this apartment. **[2 marks]**

£.............................

(d) Is this estimate reliable? Give a reason for your answer. **[1 mark]**

....

Cumulative frequency

BBC

---

② Quick quiz

Complete this statement.

A cumulative frequency diagram is a suitable way of representing ....

⓴ Drawing and using cumulative frequency diagrams Grade 6

1. The frequency table gives information about the lengths of time 100 people spent in a supermarket.

Time (t minutes)	Frequency	Cumulative frequency
$0 < t \leqslant 20$	5	5
$20 < t \leqslant 40$	11	16
$40 < t \leqslant 60$	25	
$60 < t \leqslant 80$	43	
$80 < t \leqslant 100$	13	
$100 < t \leqslant 120$	3	

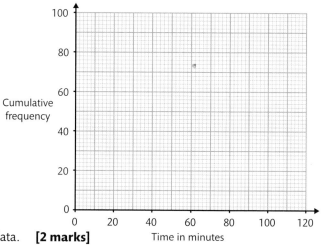

(a) On the grid, draw a cumulative frequency graph for this data. **[2 marks]**

(b) Use your graph to find an estimate for the median. **[1 marks]**

.... minutes

Work out the median by finding the $\frac{1}{2}n$th value.

(c) Use your graph to find an estimate for the interquartile range. **[2 marks]**

.... minutes

Exam focus

Work out the answer to part **(d)** by subtracting the number of people who spent less than 90 minutes from the total number of people.

(d) Use your graph to find an estimate for the number of people who spent longer than 90 minutes in the supermarket. **[2 marks]**

Number of people who spent less than 90 minutes = ...

Number of people who spent more than 90 minutes = ... − ....

....

2. The grouped frequency table gives information about the ages of 200 people at a charity event.

Age (t years)	Frequency
$0 < t \leqslant 10$	54
$10 < t \leqslant 20$	61
$20 < t \leqslant 30$	39
$30 < t \leqslant 40$	23
$40 < t \leqslant 50$	12
$50 < t \leqslant 60$	11

(a) On the grid, draw a cumulative frequency graph for your table. **[2 marks]**

(b) Use your graph to find an estimate for the interquartile range. **[2 marks]**

.... years

(c) Use the graph to find an estimate for the percentage of people aged over 36 years. **[3 marks]**

.... %

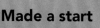 **Made a start**   **Feeling confident**   **Exam ready**

Box plots

 Quick quiz

Here is a box plot.

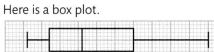

Circle the median value.

14   12   21   35

 Drawing and comparing box plots   **Grade 7**

1. The teacher in a nursery class kept a record of the amount of time, in minutes, the children spent playing in the garden last week. The table shows information about the amount of time the girls spent playing in the garden last week.

	Least	Range	Median	LQ	UQ
Time (minutes)	50	220	160	90	210

(a) On the grid below, draw a box plot to show the information in the table.   **[3 marks]**

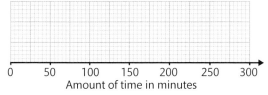
Amount of time in minutes

> Range = highest value − lowest value

> Make sure you have a box and two whiskers.

The box plot below shows information about the amount of time the boys spent playing in the garden last week.

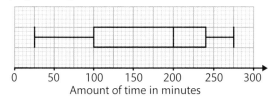
Amount of time in minutes

(b) Compare the amount of time the girls spent playing in the garden with the amount of time the boys spent playing in the garden.   **[2 marks]**

Median for girls = ...   Median for boys = ...

.... for girls = ... for boys = ...

Comparison: ....

....

> **Exam focus**
> Compare the median, the range and the interquartile range and ensure one of the comments is in context.

 Drawing and using box plots   **Grade 7**

2. The table gives information about the weights of 80 boxes.

	Lowest	Highest	LQ	IQR	Median
Weight (kg)	1.4	6.2	2.6	1.8	3.1

(a) Draw a box plot for this information.   **[3 marks]**

(b) Write down the number of boxes that weighed more than 2.6 kg.   **[2 marks]**

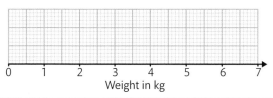
Weight in kg

....

Histograms

Circle the correct formula for frequency density.

frequency density = frequency × class width

$$\text{frequency density} = \frac{\text{frequency}}{\text{class width}}$$

$$\text{frequency density} = \frac{\text{class width}}{\text{frequency}}$$

$$\text{frequency density} = \frac{\text{frequency}^2}{\text{class width}}$$

Drawing and using histograms

Grade 8

1. The table shows some information about the lengths of time, in minutes, some adults spent cooking their dinner one evening.

Time (w minutes)	Frequency	Frequency density
$0 < w \leq 10$	7	$7 \div 10 = 0.7$
$10 < w \leq 20$	15	
$20 < w \leq 25$	16	
$25 < w \leq 30$	14	
$30 < w \leq 50$	8	

> Always work out the frequency density by adding another column to the table.

> **Exam focus**
> Remember that the area under a histogram represents frequency.

(a) Draw a histogram for the information in the table. **[3 marks]**

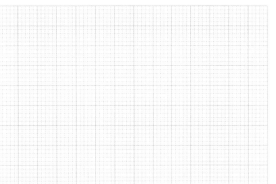

> Make sure you draw accurate scales on the time and frequency axes.

> A histogram has no gaps between the bars.

(b) Work out an estimate for the number of adults who cooked for more than 16 minutes and less than 28 minutes. **[2 marks]**

....

2. The histogram gives information about the lengths of time 200 people spent in an art gallery. Work out the probability that the time spent by an adult in the art gallery is less than 25 minutes. **[3 marks]**

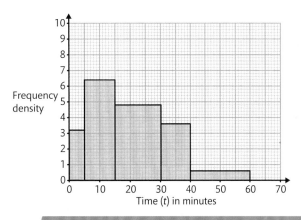

....

✓ **Made a start** ✓ **Feeling confident** ✓ **Exam ready**

Frequency polygons

---

⑤ Quick quiz

Write down the midpoint of each class interval.

(a) $0 < x \leqslant 20$ **(b)** $10 < x \leqslant 25$ **(c)** $18 < x \leqslant 30$ **(d)** $20 < x \leqslant 50$

....

---

⑮ Drawing and using frequency polygons   Grade 6

1. The table gives some information about the lengths of time, t minutes, some students took to complete a puzzle.

Length of time (mins)	$0 < t \leqslant 10$	$10 < t \leqslant 20$	$20 < t \leqslant 30$	$30 < t \leqslant 40$
Frequency	3	7	6	5

(a) Draw a frequency polygon to show this information.   **[2 marks]**

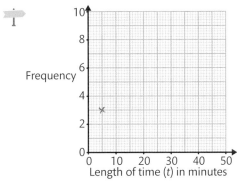

> To draw a frequency polygon, plot each point at the midpoint of the class interval.

> Join the points with straight lines. Use a ruler.

> Think about the connection between the mode of the data and the modal class interval.

(b) Write down the modal class interval.   **[1 mark]**   **(c)** Write down the class interval that contains the median.   **[1 mark]**

....

2. The frequency table gives information about the heights of some workers.

Height (cm)	$160 < h \leqslant 165$	$165 < h \leqslant 170$	$170 < h \leqslant 175$	$175 < h \leqslant 180$	$180 < h \leqslant 185$	$185 < h \leqslant 190$
Frequency	3	9	14	27	19	8

(a) Draw a frequency polygon to show this information.   **[2 marks]**

(b) One of the workers is chosen at random. Work out the probability that this worker is more than 175 cm tall.   **[2 marks]**

....

Analysing data

② Quick quiz

The median time for boys to walk home is 23 minutes and the median time for girls to walk home is 18 minutes.

Write down a contextualised comparison.

....

⑤ Interpreting cumulative frequency diagrams

Grade 6

1. The cumulative frequency graphs show information about the times taken by 100 male cyclists and 100 female cyclists to finish a race.

Use medians and interquartile ranges to compare the distribution of the times taken by the male cyclists with the distribution of the times taken by the female cyclists. **[4 marks]**

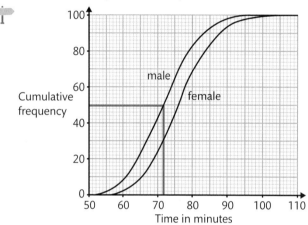

> Work out the interquartile range for the male cyclists and for the female cyclists.

> Work out the median for the male cyclists and for the female cyclists.

> Compare the medians and the interquartile ranges.

IQR for male cyclists = ... − .... = ...   Median for male cyclists = ...

IQR for female cyclists = ... − .... = ...   Median for female cyclists = ...

Comparison: ....

⑮ Interpreting data and statements

Grade 6

2. Amrit played 15 computer games. Here are the points she scored in each game:

| 28 | 29 | 29 | 29 | 30 | 31 | 31 | 33 | 34 | 34 | 34 | 37 | 38 | 39 | 39 |

Rob played the same 15 computer games. The median number of points Rob scored is 34, the interquartile range of these points is 13 and the range of these points is 18.
Who is more consistent at scoring points, Amrit or Rob? Give a reason for your answer. **[2 marks]**

....

3. Adam carried out a survey of 30 people. He found that they had a mean age of 36 years and a median age of 32 years. Adam realises he has missed out one person. This person has an age of 40. Adam decides to include this age and work out the mean age and median age of 31 people. Here are two statements about the ages of the 31 people:

Statement 1: The mean age of the 31 people is more than 36 years.
Statement 2: The median age of the 31 people is less than 32 years.
Are these statements true? Give reasons for your answers. **[2 marks]**

....

....

    Made a start   **Feeling confident**   **Exam ready**

Statistics

 Interpreting histograms   **Grade 8**

1. The histogram shows information about the times, in minutes, that some adults spent in a gym one afternoon.

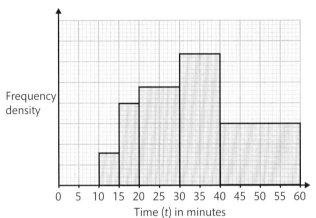

Frequency density

Time (*t*) in minutes

> Use the information to work out the frequency density between 10 and 15 minutes.

> Work out the number of adults who were in the gym between 40 and 60 minutes as a fraction of the whole number of adults who used the gym.

(a) The number of adults who spent between 10 and 15 minutes in the gym that afternoon was 2. Work out the total number of adults in the gym that afternoon.   **[3 marks]**

Exam focus

Make sure you understand what the area of a bar in a histogram represents.

....

(b) Work out the probability of an adult spending between 40 and 60 minutes in the gym. **[2 marks]**

....

 Interpreting box plots   **Grade 7**

2. These are the ages, in years, of 15 men at the local social club:

17   19   19   21   26   26   28   29   31   34   39   41   44   47   58

(a) On this grid, draw a box plot for this information.   **[3 marks]**

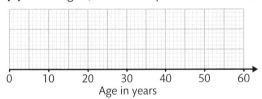

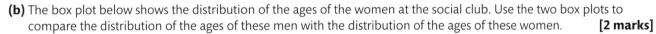

(b) The box plot below shows the distribution of the ages of the women at the social club. Use the two box plots to compare the distribution of the ages of these men with the distribution of the ages of these women.   **[2 marks]**

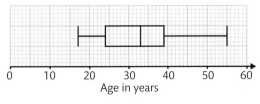

....

....

Problem-solving strategies

(10) Using trigonometry in context — Grade 7

A playground is in the shape of a triangle *ABC*.
$AB = 7.2$ m.
Angle $BAC = 50°$.
The area of the playground is 24 m².
Macey wants to put a wire fence around the playground.
The wire fence costs £9.75 per metre.
She has £235 to spend.
Does Macey have enough money to buy the wire fence?
You **must** show your working.

[5 marks]

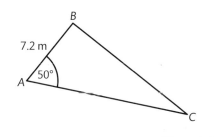

What is my plan to solve the problem?

1. What do I have to do?	*I need to work out the length of AC and BC so that I can find the perimeter of the playground. I can then work out the cost of the fence and compare the cost with £235 to see if Macey has enough money.*
2. What information do I need?	*I need to work out the lengths AC and BC.*
3. What mathematics can I do?	*I need to recall the formulae for the area of any triangle and the cosine rule.*
4. Is my solution correct?	*I will do my calculations in a logical way so that each step acts as a building block.*
5. Have I completed everything?	*I will check the answer to make sure it is sensible.*

I need to work out the length of AC.

Area of triangle $= \dfrac{1}{2}bc \sin A$

$\ldots\ldots = \dfrac{1}{2} \times \ldots\ldots \times \ldots\ldots \times \sin\ldots\ldots°$

$AC = \dfrac{\ldots\ldots \times \ldots\ldots}{\ldots\ldots \times \sin\ldots°}$

$AC = \ldots\ldots$ m

I need to work out the length of BC.

$a^2 = b^2 + c^2 - 2bc \cos A$

$BC^2 = 7.2^2 + \ldots\ldots^2 - (2 \times 7.2 \times \ldots\ldots \times \cos 50°)$

$BC^2 = 51.84 + \ldots\ldots - (2 \times 7.2 \times \ldots\ldots \times \cos 50°)$

$BC = \sqrt{\ldots\ldots\ldots}$

$BC = \ldots\ldots$ m

I need to work out the perimeter of the playground.

Perimeter $= AB + AC + BC$

Perimeter $= \ldots\ldots + \ldots\ldots + \ldots\ldots$

Perimeter $= \ldots\ldots$ m

I need to work out the cost of the fence.

Cost of fence $=$ perimeter $\times$ £9.75

Cost of fence $= \ldots\ldots \times$ £9.75

Cost of fence $=$ £$\ldots\ldots$

I need to compare the cost of the fence with the amount of money Macey has.

Cost of the fence is $\ldots\ldots$ than £235.

My conclusion

Macey $\ldots\ldots\ldots\ldots\ldots\ldots\ldots\ldots\ldots\ldots\ldots\ldots\ldots\ldots\ldots\ldots$ money.

☑ **Made a start**   ☑ **Feeling confident**   ☑ **Exam ready**

Solving number problems

1. The diagram shows a play area in the shape of triangle *ABE*, square *BCDE*, and a semicircle.

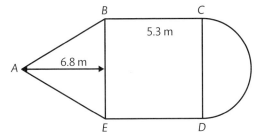

CD is the diameter of the semicircle.
Len is going to cover the play area with wood chips. The wood chips are sold in packs.
One pack of wood chips will cover 4.5 m². A pack of wood chips normally costs £23.60.
Len gets a discount of 24% off the cost of the wood chips.
Len has £220 to spend.
Does Len have enough money to buy all the wood chips he needs?
You **must** show your working.

[5 marks]

2. Ian wants to invest £9000 for 4 years in the same bank.

Bank A	Bank B
3% for the first year	4% for the first year
2% for each extra year	1.5% for each extra year

Ian wants to have as much money as possible by the end of 4 years.
Which bank should he invest his £9000 in?

[4 marks]

Solving proof problems

 Identities

1. Prove that $(n-1)^2 + n^2 + (n+1)^2 \equiv 3n^2 + 2$.

[2 marks]

2. Prove that $(n+4)^2 - (3n+4) \equiv (n+1)(n+4) + 8$.

[3 marks]

 Algebraic proof

3. Prove algebraically that $n^2 + 2 - (n-2)^2$ is always an even number. **[2 marks]**

4. Prove that $(3n+1)^2 - (3n-1)^2$ is a multiple of 6 for all positive values of n. **[2 marks]**

5. Prove algebraically that the difference between the squares of any two consecutive odd numbers is always a multiple of 8. **[4 marks]**

6. Prove algebraically that the sum of the squares of any three consecutive even numbers is always a multiple of 4. **[2 marks]**

☑ **Made a start**　　☑ **Feeling confident**　　☑ **Exam ready**

Solving geometric problems

(10) Using trigonometry   Grade 8

1. The diagram shows two isosceles triangles, ABC and DBE.
$AB = BC = x$ cm.
$DB = BE = 5$ cm.
$AC = DE$.
Angle $ABC = 45°$.

Show that $\cos\theta = 1 - \dfrac{2 - \sqrt{2}}{50}x^2$.

[5 marks]

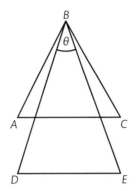

(10) Using vectors   Grade 8

2. ABD is a triangle.
E is a point on AD such that $AE:ED = 2:1$.
$\overrightarrow{AB} = \mathbf{a}$ and $AD = 3\mathbf{b}$.
B is the midpoint of AC and F is the midpoint of BD.
Prove that EFC is a straight line.
You **must** show your working.

[5 marks]

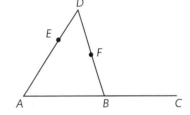

 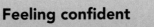

Solving algebraic problems

10   Using algebra   Grade 7

1. The diagram shows a block of wood in the shape of a cuboid.
All measurements are in centimetres.
A piece in the shape of a cube of length x cm is cut from the block of wood.
The volume of the block of wood without the cube is 32 cm^3.
Work out the volume of the cube.

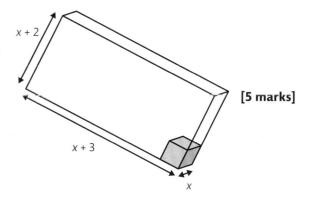

[5 marks]

.... cm^3

10   Setting up and solving equations   Grade 7

2. The diagram shows a rectangle.
The length of the rectangle is x cm.
The length of a diagonal of the rectangle is 17 cm.
The perimeter of the rectangle is 46 cm.

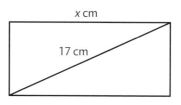

(a) Show that $x^2 - 23x + 120 = 0$.   **[3 marks]**

(b) Work out the area, in cm^2, of the rectangle.   **[3 marks]**

.... cm

☑ Made a start   ☑ Feeling confident   ☑ Exam ready

Solving statistical problems

Using conditional probability

Grade 9

1. A box contains 16 coins.
There are x gold coins in the box.
The rest of the coins are silver.
A coin is taken at random and not replaced.
Another coin is taken at random.
The probability of taking one coin of each colour is $\frac{21}{40}$.
There are more gold coins than silver coins.
A gold coin is worth £50 and a silver coin is worth £30.
Work out the total value of the coins.

[6 marks]

£...............................

Using Venn diagrams

Grade 9

2. 60 children were asked about their favourite pets.
18 children like dogs, 19 children like cats and 17 children like rabbits.
8 children like both dogs and cats.
6 children like both cats and rabbits.
7 children like both rabbits and dogs.
5 children like all 3 of these pets.

(a) Draw a Venn diagram to represent this information.

[4 marks]

A child is chosen at random.

(b) Work out the probability that the child does not like any of the pets.

[1 mark]

....

(c) Given that the child likes dogs, work out the probability that this child also likes rabbits.

[2 marks]

....

 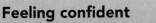

Non-calculator practice paper

Mathematics
Non-calculator (Higher Tier)

Time: 1 hour 30 minutes
Total marks: 80. Answer all questions.
You must have: ruler, protractor, pair of compasses,
pen, HB pencil, eraser
You must **not** use a calculator.

1. What is 48 as a product of its prime factors? Circle your answer. **[1 mark]**

   $2^3 \times 6$ $8 \times 3 \times 2$ $2^4 \times 3$ 16×3

2. The first five terms in a sequence are: 6   11   16   21   26

   Circle the expression for the nth term of the sequence.

   $2 + 4n$ $n^2 - 1$ $7n + 3$ $5n + 1$ **[1 mark]**

3. Sandra and Rajesh drove along the Amalfi coast for 75 km in separate cars.
   The drive took Sandra one and a half hours. Rajesh started his drive 8 minutes after Sandra had left.
   Rajesh caught up with Sandra when they both travelled 40 km.
   Both of them drove at constant speeds.
   Work out Rajesh's speed. Circle your answer.

   6 km/s   48 km/h   40 km/h   60 km/h   **[5 marks]**

4. (a) The table shows some information about the times, in minutes, 20 people took to get to work.

Time (t minutes)	$0 < t \leq 20$	$20 < t \leq 40$	$40 < t \leq 60$	$60 < t \leq 80$	$80 < t \leq 100$
Frequency	6	4	3	5	2

   Estimate the mean. Circle your answer.

   40   43   33   53   **[3 marks]**

   (b) Explain why your answer is an estimate. **[1 mark]**

5. Ariana is x years old. Samir is twice as old as Ariana. Carla is 4 years younger than Samir.
   The sum of all their ages is 56 years.
   Work out the ages of Ariana, Samir, and Carla. **[4 marks]**

6. DAB and DCB are isosceles triangles.
   $AD = AB$.
   $BD = DC$.
   AB is parallel to DC.
   Work out the size of angle x. Give reasons for your answer. **[4 marks]**

   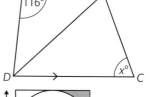

7. The diagram shows a circle drawn inside a square.
   The square has a side of length 8 cm.
   Work out the shaded area.
   Give your answer in terms of π. **[4 marks]**

   8 cm

   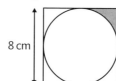

8. $x = 0.5\dot{1}\dot{8}$

   Prove algebraically that x can be written as $\dfrac{57}{110}$. **[3 marks]**

9. The table gives information about the lengths and frequencies of the telephone calls received by John.

Length of call (t mins)	$0<t\leqslant 5$	$5<t\leqslant 10$	$10<t\leqslant 15$	$15<t\leqslant 20$	$20<t\leqslant 25$
Frequency	20	45	16	12	6

John draws a frequency polygon using this information.

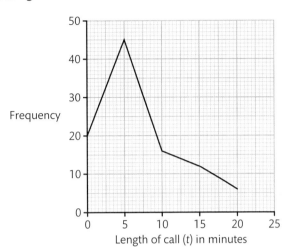

Write down one thing that is wrong with John's frequency polygon. **[1 mark]**

10. Here is a rectangle.
All measurements are in centimetres.
Given that the value of the perimeter of the rectangle
is equal to the value of the area of the rectangle, work out the value of x. **[4 marks]**

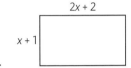

11. Abi says that 0.073 is 1000 times bigger than 7.3×10^{-5}. Is she correct? Tick a box.

Yes ☐   No ☐

Give a reason for your answer. **[2 marks]**

12. **(a)** Write down the value of $81^{\frac{1}{2}}$. **[1 mark]**

(b) Work out the value of $64^{\frac{2}{3}}$. **[2 marks]**

13. 4 adult tickets and 3 child tickets cost a total of £27.75. 5 adult tickets and 2 child tickets cost a total of £29.00.
Work out the cost of one adult ticket and the cost of one child ticket. **[4 marks]**

14. The table below shows information about the ages, in years, of some women at a book club.

	Least	Lower quartile	Median	Upper quartile	Greatest
Age in years	26	30	38	52	60

(a) On graph paper, draw a box plot to show the information in the table. **[3 marks]**

The box plot below shows the distribution of the ages of the men at the book club.

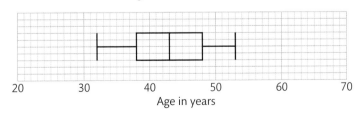

(b) Compare the distribution of ages of the women with the distribution of ages of the men. **[2 marks]**
Circle the statement that is **not** true.

The median is greater for the men.   The range in the ages of the women is greater.

The interquartile range is greater for the men.   The men are generally older.

121

15. A company makes cushions that are either black or white. Each day, Tom takes a sample of 10 cushions to check the quality. The proportion of the black cushions in his sample must be the same as the proportion of the black cushions made that day. On Thursday, 350 cushions were made. Tom worked out that he needed exactly 7 black cushions in his sample.
(a) Work out the total number of black cushions that were made on Thursday. **[2 marks]**

On Friday, 400 cushions were made. The number of white cushions Tom needs in his sample is 8, rounded to the nearest whole number.

(b) Circle the upper bound of the number of white cushions made on Friday. **[2 marks]**

$$x > 340 \qquad x < 340 \qquad x \leqslant 340 \qquad x \geqslant 340$$

16. $a + b : b - 2a = t : 3$

Show that $a = \dfrac{b(t - 3)}{3 + 2t}$. **[3 marks]**

17. y is directly proportional to x^3. When $x = \dfrac{1}{2}$, $y = 2\dfrac{3}{4}$.
Give a formula for y in terms of x. **[3 marks]**

18. Prove that $(n+2)^2 + n^2 + (n-2)^2 \equiv 3n^2 + 8$. **[2 marks]**

19. The diagram shows triangles A and B.

Triangle A can be mapped to triangle B by a single transformation.

Jess says the only single transformation is a translation of $\begin{pmatrix} 6 \\ 0 \end{pmatrix}$.

Is she correct? Tick a box.

Yes ☐   No ☐

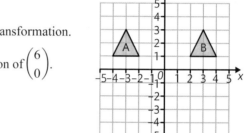

Give a reason for your answer. **[2 marks]**

20. The points $A(12, 1)$ and $B(-3, 6)$ are on the line with equation $y = -\dfrac{1}{3}x + 5$. M is the midpoint of AB.

Give an equation of the line through M that is perpendicular to $y = -\dfrac{1}{3}x + 5$. **[4 marks]**

21. The table shows some values of x and y that satisfy the equation $y = a\sin x° + b$.

x	0	30	45	90	120
y	1	2	$1 + \sqrt{2}$	3	$1 + \sqrt{3}$

Work out the value of y when $x = 60$. **[4 marks]**

22. The expression $\dfrac{4 - \sqrt{12}}{\sqrt{3} - 1}$ can be written in the form $a\sqrt{3} + b$ where a and b are integers.
Work out the values of a and b. **[3 marks]**

23. Here are a trapezium and a right-angled triangle.
All measurements are in centimetres.
The area of the triangle is greater than the area of the trapezium.
Work out the set of possible values of x.

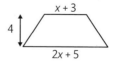

[5 marks]

24. The expression $x^2 - 4x - 1$ can be written in the form $(x - a)^2 + b$ for all values of x.
(a) Work out the value of a and the value of b. **[3 marks]**

The diagram shows part of the curve with equation $y = f(x)$, where $f(x) = x^2 - 4x - 1$.
M is the minimum point of this curve.

(b) Write down the coordinates of the minimum point of the curve with equation
  (i) $y = f(x) + 4$
  (ii) $y = -f(x)$. **[2 marks]**

Calculator practice paper

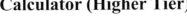

Mathematics
Calculator (Higher Tier)

Time: 1 hour 30 minutes
Total marks: 80. Answer all questions.
You must have: calculator, ruler, protractor, pair of compasses,
pen, HB pencil, eraser

Exam focus
You will be allowed to use a
calculator in Paper 2 and Paper 3
of your GCSE Maths exam.

1. Solve $7x - 5 = 2(x + 5)$. Circle your answer.

   $x = 3$ $x = 2$ $x = 1$ $x = \dfrac{5}{3}$ **[1 mark]**

2. Circle the expression that is equivalent to $(5x^3y^2)^2$.

   $10x^5y^4$ $25x^6y^4$ $25x^9y^4$ $25x^5y^4$ **[1 mark]**

3. What is 700 million in standard form? Circle your answer.

   700×10^6 7.0×10^7 7×10^8 0.7×10^9 **[1 mark]**

4. The equation of a curve is $y = (x-4)^2 + 5$. Circle the coordinates of the turning point.

   $(4, -5)$ $(4, 5)$ $(-4, -5)$ $(-4, 5)$ **[1 mark]**

5. David buys 2 boxes of mangoes.
   Each box contains 8 mangoes. Each box costs £6.40. He sells each mango for £1.55.
   Work out David's profit as a percentage. Give your answer correct to 1 decimal place.   **[3 marks]**

6. Hannah weighs a block of wood and finds it has a mass of 8 kg. Hannah assumes the volume of the block is 7200 cm³.

   (a) Use her assumption to work out the density of the block.   **[1 mark]**

   In fact, the block has a higher volume than 7200 cm².

   (b) How does this fact affect the density of the block?   **[3 marks]**

7. A box contains only black counters, white counters and grey counters.
   There are three times as many black counters as white counters and five times as many grey counters as black counters.
   A counter is taken at random from the box. Work out the probability that the counter is white.   **[3 marks]**

8. **(a)** Rotate triangle T 180° about the origin.
   Label the new triangle A.   **[1 mark]**

   (b) Translate triangle T by the vector $\begin{pmatrix} -1 \\ -4 \end{pmatrix}$.
   Label the new triangle B.   **[1 mark]**

   (c) Circle the coordinates that are **not** one of the vertices of triangle B.

   $(-4, 0)$ $(-4, -3)$ $(-2, 0)$ $(-2, -3)$ **[1 mark]**

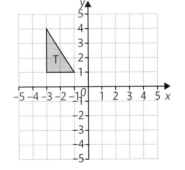

9. **(a)** $m^4 \times m^x = m^{11}$
   Work out the value of x.   **[1 mark]**

   (b) $(n^y)^4 = n^{12}$
   Work out the value of y.   **[1 mark]**

10. Use your calculator to work out $\dfrac{\sqrt{57.2 - 18.5}}{4.49 \times 0.6}$.

    Write down all the figures on your calculator display.   **[2 marks]**

11. *ABC* is a triangle.
Work out the size of angle *BCD*.
Give your answer to 3 significant figures.

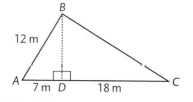

[4 marks]

12. An oil company wants to remove oil from an oil slick.
They have a choice of two pumps.

Penn Pump
Each pump can pump 40 gallons in 1 minute.

Wulfrun Pump
One pump can pump all the oil in 400 hours.

The oil slick contains 500 000 gallons of oil. The company can use three Penn pumps or four Wulfrun pumps.
The company wants to pump all the oil out of the slick as quickly as possible.
Should the company use the three Penn pumps or the four Wulfrun pumps? You **must** show your working.   **[5 marks]**

13. The graph shows information about the distance travelled by a truck.
The graph is a straight line.

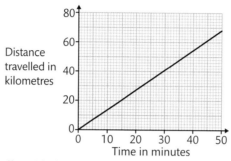

(a) Work out the gradient of the straight line. Circle your answer.

1.4   1.36   1.28   1.2   **[2 marks]**

(b) Write down a practical interpretation of the value you calculated in part (a).   **[1 mark]**

14. ℰ = {odd numbers less than 30}
A = {3, 9, 15, 21, 27}
B = {5, 15, 25}

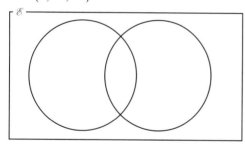

Complete the Venn diagram to represent this information.   **[4 marks]**

15. *AB* and *BC* are sides of a regular polygon. The regular polygon has 15 sides.
A line is drawn from point *A* to point *C* to form a triangle.
Work out the size of angle *BAC*. You **must** show your working.

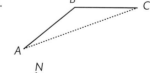

[3 marks]

16. *ONQ* is a sector of a circle with centre *O* and radius 12 cm.
A is the point on *ON* and *B* is the point on *OQ* such that *AOB*
is an equilateral triangle of side 6.5 cm.
Work out the area of the shaded region.
Give your answer to 1 decimal place.

[4 marks]

17. Adam bought a painting in January 2010 for £75 000. Each year, the value of the painting increased by 3%.
(a) Work out the value of the painting in January 2017. Give your answer to the nearest £100.   **[2 marks]**

Eve bought a different painting in January 2010 for £125 000.
After eight years, the value of this painting had increased to £300 000. This is an increase of *x*% each year.

(b) Work out the value of *x*. Give your answer to 1 decimal place.   **[3 marks]**

18. On the grid, shade the region defined by these inequalities:

$x + y < 5$, $x > -2$, $y > 1$.

Mark this region with the letter R.

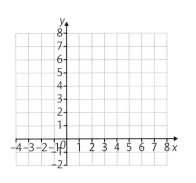

[3 marks]

19. The table shows some information about the lengths of time some children spent on their homework.

Time (t minutes)	Frequency
$0 < t \leqslant 10$	8
$10 < t \leqslant 20$	16
$20 < t \leqslant 25$	15
$25 < t \leqslant 30$	12
$30 < t \leqslant 50$	8

(a) Draw a histogram for the information in the table on graph paper. **[3 marks]**
(b) Circle the fraction of the children who spent between 20 minutes and 35 minutes on their homework. **[2 marks]**

$$\frac{27}{59} \qquad \frac{35}{59} \qquad \frac{29}{59} \qquad \frac{32}{59}$$

20. Govind is choosing a shirt and a jumper for his school uniform. There are 12 different types of shirts and a selection of different jumpers. Govind says, "There are 195 different combinations of one shirt and one jumper."
Is Govind correct? Give a reason for your answer. **[2 marks]**

21. Carl has been asked to solve equation $4(x-1)^2 - 7 = 0$. His solution is as follows:

$4(x-1)^2 = 7$ 　　　　　add 7 to both sides

$(x-1)^2 = \dfrac{7}{4}$ 　　　　　divide both sides by 4

$x - 1 = \sqrt{\dfrac{7}{4}}$ 　　　　　square root both sides

$x = 1 + \sqrt{\dfrac{7}{4}}$ 　　　　　add 1 to both sides

State two reasons why Carl has not been awarded full marks. **[2 marks]**

22. $A(-2, -5)$, $B(2, 5)$ and $C(6, -1)$ are the vertices of a triangle. M is the midpoint of AB and N is the midpoint of BC.
Show that MN is parallel to AC. You **must** show your working. **[4 marks]**

23. There are six girls and nine boys in a badminton club.
Dev is going to pick three players at random from the badminton club.
Work out the probability that Dev will pick three boys or three girls for the team. **[4 marks]**

24. Prove algebraically that the straight line with equation $x - 3y = 20$ is a tangent to the circle with equation $x^2 + y^2 = 40$. **[5 marks]**

25. **(a)** The first three terms of an arithmetic sequence are $(\sqrt{x} - 2), 2, (\sqrt{x} + 2)$.
　　Work out the value of x. You **must** show your working. **[3 marks]**
(b) Give an expression for the nth term of this sequence. **[2 marks]**
(c) Is 99 a term in this sequence? Give a reason for your answer. **[1 mark]**

Answers

Page 1 Fractions, decimals and percentages

Quick quiz:

1. $\dfrac{1}{10}$

2. **(a)** 31.5 **(b)** 57.6 **(c)** 72 **(d)** 100

Questions:

1. 135

2. **(a) (i)** 41% **(ii)** 15% **(b)** 36

3. $x = 0.1\,787\,878\,787$

   $10x = 1.7\,878\,787\,878$

   $1000x = 178.787\,878$

   Subtracting: $990x = 177$

   $x = \dfrac{177}{990} = \dfrac{59}{330}$

Page 2 Manipulating fractions

Quick quiz: Adding or subtracting fractions: Find equivalent fractions with the same denominator.

Multiplying fractions: Multiply the numerators and multiply the denominators.

Dividing fractions: Invert the second fraction then multiply.

Questions:

1. **(a)** $\dfrac{5}{14}$ **(b)** $\dfrac{6}{11}$ **(c)** $1\dfrac{9}{10}$

2. **(a)** $7\dfrac{31}{40}$ **(b)** $1\dfrac{19}{21}$ **(c)** $2\dfrac{1}{3}$

3. 90 **4.** $\dfrac{4}{15}$ of $225 = 60$ **5.** $\dfrac{13}{24}$

Page 3 Percentage change

Quick quiz:

1. 100 **2.** 6 **3.** 20 **4.** 45

Questions:

1. **(a)** 13.5% **(b)** 16.7% **(c)** 49.9%
2. **(a)** 1075.2 **(b)** 195.16 **(c)** £92.075
3. Yes, as he reaches 30%.
4. Hotel 1 is £7828 and Hotel 2 is £8925, so Hotel 1 is cheaper.

Page 4 Reverse percentages

Quick quiz:

1.12 = An increase of 12%   1.105 = An increase of 10.5%

0.85 = A decrease of 15%   0.972 = A decrease of 2.8%

Questions:

1. £1200 **2.** £144 **3.** 31 minutes
4. Fixed bond: £1930; ISA: £1884. The fixed bond grew more.

Page 5 Growth and decay

Quick quiz:

(a) 1.15 **(b)** 0.82 **(c)** 1.0235 **(d)** 0.931

Questions:

1. £1952.62 **2.** $n = 3$ **3.** 2.5%
4. £2856.37 **5.** 2533

Page 6 Estimation and counting

Quick quiz: (a) 80 **(b)** 200 **(c)** 0.2 **(d)** 0.5

Questions:

1. **(a)** 450 **(b)** Lisa is correct because, although $25 \times 24 = 600$, each pair of women has been counted twice.

2. 270
3. **(a)** 4000 **(b)** 4
4. **(a)** 75 cm²
   (b) Underestimate as the values of π and r are rounded down.
5. 8000

Page 7 Upper and lower bounds

Quick quiz:

(a) add **(b)** subtract

Questions:

1. **(a)** LB: 1500 m; UB: 2500 m
   (b) LB: 0.55 kg; UB: 0.65 kg
   (c) LB: 4.5 s; UB: 5.5 s
   (d) LB: 9.5 miles; UB: 10.5 miles
2. 2.8 **3.** 7.87 m/s
4. The volume of drink could be 250 ml and the capacity of the bottle could be 249.95 ml, so yes, Tom is correct.

Page 8 Accuracy and error

Quick quiz:

1. **(a)** 24.35 m **(b)** 24.25 m
2. $17.5 \leqslant l < 18.5$

Questions:

1. Density = 2.4 g/cm³ to 1 d.p. This is the appropriate degree of accuracy because both values round to the same value when rounded to 1 d.p.
2. $P = 3.06$; UB and LB both round to the same value when rounded to 2 decimal places.
3. $t = 4.2$ seconds; UB and LB both round to the same value when rounded to 1 d.p.

Page 9 Factors and primes

Quick quiz:

(a) $2^3 \times 3^2 \times 5$ **(b)** $5^2 \times 7 \times 11^3$

Questions:

1. $2^3 \times 3^2$
2. $2^2 \times 3^2 \times 5$
3. **(a)** 3×5^2 **(b)** 15 **(c)** 450
4. **(a)** 20 **(b)** 600
5. 18 and 45 **6.** £60.25

Page 10 Standard form
Quick quiz:
1. **(a)** 10^3 **(b)** 10^5 **(c)** 10^8 **(d)** 10^9
2. $0.4 \times 10^{-3}, 48 \times 10^2$

Questions:
1. 4.5×10^5
2. **(a)** 0.00078 **(b)** 6×10
3. $-4.5 \times 10^{-2}, 45 \times 10^{-4}, 0.0045 \times 10^6, 45 \times 10^3, 4.5 \times 10^5$
4. No, as 8 cm is greater than 7.5 cm.
5. 1.37×10^9 s

Page 11 Surds
Quick quiz:
(a) 7 **(b)** 72 **(c)** 48 **(d)** 25

Questions:
1. $4\sqrt{2}$ 2. $4\sqrt{7}$ 3. $5 + 2\sqrt{3}$
4. $\dfrac{3 - \sqrt{6}}{18}$ cm²   5. $4\sqrt{2}$ m

Page 12 Exam skills: Number
1. £73.50   2. 4.5
3. No, his answer should be $2\sqrt{3}$.
4. $a = 2.6$ to 1 decimal place because the UB and LB both round to the same value when rounded to 1 decimal place.

Page 13 Algebraic expressions
Quick quiz:
1. **(a)** $14x$ **(b)** $4x - 20$
2. **(a)** $x(x + 4)$ **(b)** $(x - 3)(x + 3)$

Questions:
1. $3y - 2x$ 2. $2x(2x - 3)$
3. $6x^2 + 5x - 21$
4. **(a)** $5x$ **(b)** $x^2 - 4x - 32$ **(c)** $2n^2 + 2n + 13$
5. **(a)** $3xy(5x^2 - 6y)$ **(b)** $5x^2y^3(3x^2y^2 - 7)$
 (c) $(2a + b)(x - y)$
6. **(a)** $(n + 4)^2 - (n - 4)^2 = n^2 + 8n + 16 - (n^2 - 8n + 16)$
 $= 16n = 2 \times 8n$
 (b) $(n + 1)^2 - n^2 = n^2 + 2n + 1 - n^2$
 $= 2n + 1 = n + (n + 1)$

Page 14 Algebraic formulae
Quick quiz:
1. **(a)** $x^2 + 6x$ **(b)** $x^2 - x - 6$
2. $h = \dfrac{2A}{b}$
3. **(a)** $3x + 3$ **(b)** $4x - 2$

Questions:
1. $T = 6x + 15y$
2. Base: $(12x - 1)(x + 3) = 12x^2 + 35x - 3$
 Top: $(4x - 1)(x + 3) = 4x^2 + 11x - 3$
 Sides: $2(5x)(x + 3) = 10x^2 + 30x$
 Front and back: $2(3x)(8x - 1) = 48x^2 - 6x$
 Total surface area $= (12 + 4 + 10 + 48)x^2 +$
 $(35 + 11 + 30 - 6)x - 3 - 3 = 74x^2 + 70x - 6$
3. $A = x^2 + 6x + 7$

Page 15 Laws of indices
Quick quiz:
(a) a^4 **(b)** a^4 **(c)** $18a^2b$ **(d)** $3a^2b^3$

Questions:
1. **(a)** x^4 **(b)** $18x^6y^4$ **(c)** $27x^6y^9$ **(d)** $5x^2y^3$
2. **(a)** $15x^3y^4$ **(b)** $\dfrac{5x^4(x + 1)^2}{3}$ **(c)** $5x^5y^2$ **(d)** $16x^{24}y^{16}$
3. $n = 4$
4. **(a)** $x = -16$ **(b)** $x = 20$

Page 16 Combining indices
Quick quiz:
(a) 5 **(b)** 9 **(c)** 3 **(d)** 4

Questions:
1. 3^{10}
2. $\dfrac{1}{8}$
3. **(a)** 64 **(b)** 16 **(c)** 9
4. **(a)** $\dfrac{1}{9}$ **(b)** $\dfrac{1}{3}$ **(c)** $\dfrac{1}{8}$
5. **(a)** $\dfrac{8}{27}$ **(b)** $\dfrac{8}{125}$ **(c)** $\dfrac{4}{9}$
6. **(a)** $n = 0$ **(b)** $n = -2$ **(c)** $n = -2$ **(d)** $n = 3.5$

Page 17 Linear equations
Quick quiz
$x = \dfrac{y}{3p}$

Questions:
1. **(a)** $x = \dfrac{11}{6}$ **(b)** $x = -\dfrac{25}{7}$ **(c)** $x = 1$ **(d)** $y = 6$
 (e) $x = -\dfrac{7}{3}$ **(f)** $x = 20$
2. **(a)** $x = \dfrac{7}{10}$ **(b)** $x = 6$
3. A sent 19, B sent 57, C sent 10.
4. 6

Page 18 Linear equations and fractions
Quick quiz:
(a) $x = 5$ **(b)** $x = 18$

Questions:
1. $x = \dfrac{4}{7}$ 2. $x = \dfrac{11}{2}$ 3. $x = -\dfrac{4}{5}$
4. $x = -7$ 5. $x = -\dfrac{11}{5}$
6. 16 400

Page 19 Simultaneous equations
Quick quiz:
(a) $x = 6, y = 4$ **(b)** $x = -1, y = \dfrac{9}{10}$

Questions:
1. $x = -7, y = -4$ 2. $x = 5, y = -2$
3. $x = 4, y = 3$
4. Shirt = £12.50, trousers = £18.00

Page 20 Quadratic equations

Quick quiz:

(a) 2 and 10   **(b)** 5 and −3

(c) −1 and −4   **(d)** 4 and −5

Questions:

1. **(a)** $x = 0$ or $x = 4$ **(b)** $x = 1$ or $x = 10$

    (c) $x = \dfrac{1}{3}$ or $x = -\dfrac{7}{3}$

2. **(a)** $x = 9$ or $x = -4$ **(b)** $x = 5$ or $x = 3$

3. **(a)** $x = \dfrac{4}{3}$ or $x = -\dfrac{3}{4}$ **(b)** $x = 3$ or $x = -\dfrac{7}{3}$

4. $x = 2$

Page 21 Mixed simultaneous equations

Quick quiz:

(a) $x^2 - 10x + 6 = 0$ **(b)** $x^2 - 5x - 8 = 0$

(c) $x^2 + 4x - 10 = 0$

Questions:

1. $x = 2, y = 7$ or $x = 3, y = 9$

2. $x = -4, y = \dfrac{1}{2}$ or $x = \dfrac{5}{2}, y = -\dfrac{11}{4}$

3. $x = -10, y = 7$ or $x = 2, y = 1$

4. $x = 4, y = -3$ or $x = -3, y = 4$

Page 22 Completing the square

Quick quiz:

(a) 1   **(b)** −40   **(c)** $\dfrac{11}{4}$ **(d)** $-\dfrac{57}{4}$

Questions:

1. $a = 5, b = -33$ 2. $p = 2, q = 1$

3. $p = \dfrac{5}{2}, q = -\dfrac{13}{4}$

4. **(a)** $p = 4, q = 2$ **(b)** $(4, 2)$

5. **(a)** $a = 6, b = -11$ **(b)** −11

6. $a = 6, b = 14$

Page 23 The quadratic formula

Quick quiz:

(a) −23   **(b)** 112   **(c)** −44   **(d)** 65

Questions:

1. $x = -1.44$ or $x = -5.56$ 2. $x = 0.29$ or $x = -2.29$

3. $x = -0.56$ or $x = 3.56$ 4. $x = 1.07$ or $x = -1.67$

5. $x = 2.23$ or $x = 10.77$ 6. $x = 4.39$

Page 24 Linear inequalities

Quick quiz:

< less than   > greater than

≤ less than or equal to   ≥ greater than or equal to

Questions:

1. **(a)** $x > 6$ **(b)** $x \leqslant -4.5$ **(c)** $x > 3$

2.

3. $x < \dfrac{3}{2}$ 4. −2, −1, 0, 1, 2

5. **(a)** $32b + 45c \leqslant 1000$ **(b)** 12   6. 5

Page 25 Quadratic inequalities

Quick quiz:

(a) $x(x - 3)$ **(b)** $(x + 4)(x + 2)$ **(c)** $(2x - 1)(x + 4)$

Questions:

1. $x \leqslant 3$ or $x \geqslant 5$ 2. $-4 \leqslant x \leqslant 8$ 3. $\{x : x < 0\} \cup \{x : x > 8\}$

4. **(a)** $x + 4 + x + 4 + x + x > 12, 4x + 8 > 12, 4x > 4,$
       $x > 1$

    (b) (i) $x(x + 4) < 32$ **(ii)** $-8 < x < 4$

    (c) $1 < x < 4$

Page 26 Arithmetic sequences

Quick quiz:

(a) 11, 14, 17   **(b)** 91, 88, 85   **(c)** 31, 36, 41

Questions:

1. 1 4 7 10 13

2. **(a)** $5n + 3$ **(b)** No, as $n = 49.75$ is not an integer.

3. **(a)** No, as 35.333... is not an integer.   **(b)** $6n + 5$

4. $X = 1, 5, 9, 13, 17, 21, ...; Y = 11, 8, 5, 2, ...$
   Since X is increasing and Y is decreasing, the only term
   that is in both sequences is 5.

5. nth term is $4n - 1$. Squaring the $(n + 1)$th and nth
   terms and subtracting gives:
   $$(4n + 3)^2 - (4n - 1)^2 = 16n^2 + 24n + 9 - (16n^2 - 8n + 1)$$
   $$= 32n + 8 = 8(4n + 1).$$

Page 27 Quadratic sequences

Quick quiz:

(a) 2   **(b)** 6   **(c)** 1

Questions:

1. 1, 4, 16, 64, 256

2. $n^2 + 3n + 1$ 3. $n^2 + n + 7$

4. 5, 8, 14, 23 because the second differences are all the
   same.

5. $2n^2 + 8n - 7$

Page 28 Sequence problems

Quick quiz:

(a) 90, 88, 86   **(b)** 36, 49, 64

(c) 8, 13, 21   **(d)** 64, 128, 256

Questions:

1. $a = -4$ and $b = 19$

2. **(a)** 123
       (b) 4th $= a + 2b$, 5th $= 2a + 3b$, 6th $= 3a + 5b$,
           7th $= 5a + 8b$, 8th $= 8a + 13b$
       (c) $a = 2$ and $b = 3$

3. **(a)** 4th $= a + 4b$, 5th $= 2a + 6b$,
           6th $= 3a + 10b$, 7th $= 5a + 16b$
       (b) $a = 2, b = 3$

4. **(a)** 3   9   27   81   **(b)** 81

Page 29 Drawing straight-line graphs

Quick quiz:

1. −4   2. **(a)** 13   **(b)** −14

Questions:

1. $y = -\dfrac{6}{5}x + 6$

2.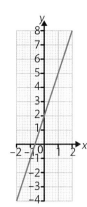

3.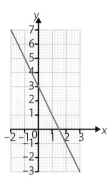

4. (a) Gradient = 2, so the water heats up 2 °C every second

(b) $y = 2x + 20$

Page 30 Equations of straight lines

Quick quiz:

(a) $(6, 7)$ **(b)** $(2, 7)$

Questions:

1. $y = -5x + 22$ **2.** $y = 2x + 5$

3. (a) $(1, 7)$ **(b)** $y = -\dfrac{2}{3}x + \dfrac{23}{3}$

4. (a) $y = 4x + 8$ **(b)** $3y - 2x = -17$

Page 31 Parallel and perpendicular lines

Quick quiz:

$y = 6x + 4$

Questions:

1. $y = -\dfrac{1}{2}x + \dfrac{5}{2}$

2. (a) $y = \dfrac{3}{2}x + 2$ **(b)** $y = -\dfrac{2}{3}x + \dfrac{14}{3}$

3. $y = -\dfrac{1}{3}x + 3$

4. Yes, because gradient of line N is $\dfrac{-1 - 1}{4 - 1} = -\dfrac{2}{3}$

and gradient of other line is $\dfrac{6}{4}$

$-\dfrac{2}{3} \times \dfrac{6}{4} = -1$

5. Gradient of line A is $\dfrac{5}{4}$, gradient of line B is $\dfrac{5}{3}$, gradient

of line C is $\dfrac{8 - 3}{2 - (-2)} = \dfrac{5}{4}$; so lines A and C are parallel.

Page 32 Quadratic graphs

Quick quiz:

From left to right: $y = 2 + 4x - x^2$ $y = 1 - 2x$
$y = 3x - 2$ $y = x^2 - 6x - 7$

Questions:

1. (a)

x	−1	0	1	2	3	4	5
y	7	2	−1	−2	−1	2	7

(b)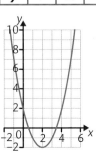

(c) approximately $x = 3.4$ and $x = 0.6$

2. (a)

x	−1	0	1	2	3	4	5
y	9	3	−1	−3	−3	−1	3

(b)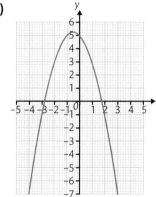

(c) approximately $x = 4.3$ and $x = 0.7$

3. (a)

x	−4	−3	−2	−1	0	1	2	3
y	−7	−1	3	5	5	3	−1	−7

(b)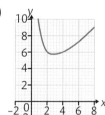

(c) approximately $x = -2.8$ and $x = 1.8$

Page 33 Cubic and reciprocal graphs

Quick quiz:

From left to right: $y = \dfrac{1}{x}$ $\quad y = x^3$ $\quad y = -\dfrac{1}{x}$ $\quad y = -x^3$

Questions:

1. (a)

x	1	1.5	2	2.5	3	4	6	8
y	9	6.8	6	5.7	5.7	6	7.3	9

(b)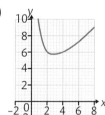

(c) approximately $x = 5.6$ and $x = 1.4$

2. (a)

x	−2	−1	0	1	2
y	−2	3	2	1	6

(b)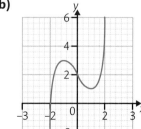

(c) approximately $x = -1.8$

3. (a)

x	0.5	1	2	4	5	8
y	8	4	2	1	0.8	0.5

(b)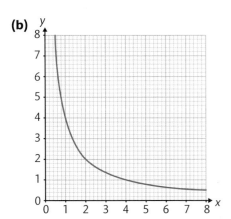

Page 34 Real-life graphs
Quick quiz:

(a) speed **(b)** horizontal line

Questions:

1. **(a)** 36 km/h **(b)**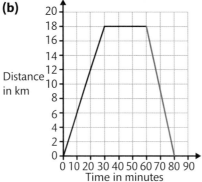

   (c) 30 minutes

2. **(a)**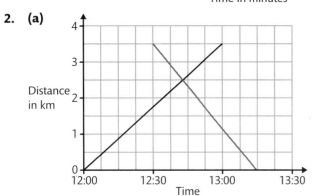

   (b) 2.5 km

3. **(a)** $F = \dfrac{9}{5}C + 32$ **(b)** Manchester

Page 35 Trigonometric graphs
Quick quiz:

1. same, 90° 2. 360°

Questions:

1. **(a)** $\dfrac{\sqrt{2}}{2}$ **(b)** $-\dfrac{\sqrt{2}}{2}$ **(c)** $-\dfrac{\sqrt{2}}{2}$

2. **(a)** 60° **(b)** **(c)** 240°

3. **(a)** 60° **(b)**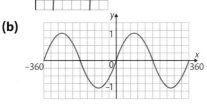

   (c) 240°, 300°

130

4. **(a)** 105–110°, 250–255° **(b)** 39–43°, 317–321°
   (c) 64–68°, 292–296°

Page 36 Inequalities on graphs
Quick quiz:

(a) dashed line **(b)** solid line

Questions:

1.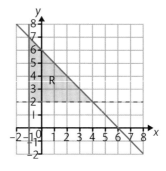

2.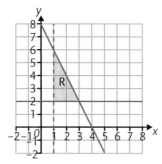

3.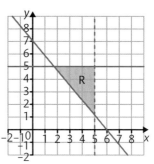

4. $x \geqslant -2$, $x \leqslant 4$, $y < 3$ and $y \geqslant 1$

Page 37 Using quadratic graphs
Quick quiz:

(a) (ii) **(b)** (iii) **(c)** (i)

Questions:

1. **(a)**

x	−2	−1	0	1	2	3	4
y	7	2	−1	−2	−1	2	7

   (b) and **(c)**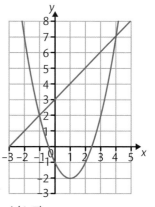

   (d) (−1, 2) and (4, 7)

2. **(a)**

x	−1	0	1	2	3	4	5
y	6	2	0	0	2	6	12

(b)

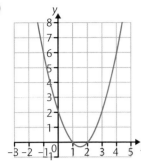

(c) approximately $x = 0.3$ and $x = 3.7$

4.

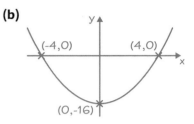

5. (a) $(x + 4)(x - 4)$ **(b)**

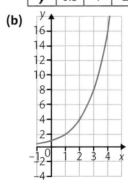

Page 38 Turning points
Quick quiz:

Questions:

1. **(a)** $(x - 5)^2 - 22$ **(b)** $(5, -22)$
2. **(a)** $2(x + 2)^2 + 7$ **(b)** $(-2, 7)$
3. $y = x^2 + 8x + 14$
4. **(a)** $2(x - 1)^2 + 5$
   (b) Minimum point is $(1, 5)$, so the curve doesn't cross the x–axis.
5. $(2 + \sqrt{6}, 0)$ and $(2 - \sqrt{6}, 0)$

Page 39 Sketching graphs
Quick quiz:

(a) $x = \pm 5$ **(b)** $x = 4, x = 5$ **(c)** $x = -2, x = 9$

Questions:

1. **(a)** $(x - 4)^2 + 3$ **(b)**

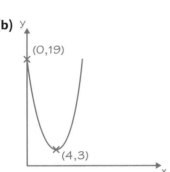

2. **(a)** $(x - 4)^2 - 4$ **(b)**

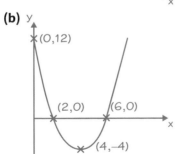

3. **(a)** $x(x - 4)(x + 3)$ **(b)**

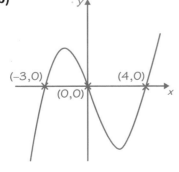

Page 40 Exponential graphs
Quick quiz:

(a) decreasing, less than 1   **(b)** increasing, more than 1

Questions:

1. **(a)**

x	-1	0	1	2	3	4
y	0.5	1	2	4	8	16

(b)

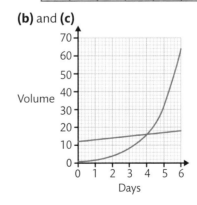

2. **(a)**

t	0	1	2	3	4	5	6
V	1	2	4	8	16	32	64

(b) and (c)

(d) 4 days

Page 41 Gradients of curves
Quick quiz:

1. $\dfrac{\text{change in vertical value}}{\text{change in horizontal value}}$ 2. **(a)** $-0.333...$ **(b)** 3

Questions:

1. **(a)** 0.3 cm/s   **(b)** 0.28 cm/s
   (c) The depth increases by 0.28 cm per second.
2. **(a)** £4600–£4800 per year   **(b)** £4500–£4700 per year

Page 42 Velocity-time graphs

Quick quiz:

(a) acceleration **(b)** distance travelled

Questions:

1. **(a)** $0.4\,\text{m/s}^2$ **(b)** $150\,\text{m}$
2. **(a)** 6 seconds **(b)** 4.2 seconds and 8 seconds
   (c) $-0.6\,\text{m/s}^2$, Asha is decelerating.
3. **(a)** $35\,\text{m/s}$ **(b)** 7.2 seconds **(c)** $6.3\text{–}6.9\,\text{m/s}^2$

Page 43 Areas under curves

Quick quiz:

$17.5\,\text{cm}^2$

Questions:

1. **(a)** $1590\,\text{m}$
   (b) It is an underestimate as the area of each trapezium is below the curve.
2. **(a)** $21.2\,\text{m}^3$
   (b) It is an overestimate as the area of each trapezium is above the curve.
3. **(a)** $7.5\,\text{kW}$
   (b) It is an underestimate as the area of each trapezium is below the curve.

Page 44 Transforming graphs

Quick quiz:

(a) x-axis **(b)** y-axis

Questions:

1. $y = -x^2 - 6x + 1$
2. **(a) (i)** $(2, 15)$ **(ii)** $(6, 19)$ **(iii)** $(-6, 15)$ **(iv)** $(6, -15)$
   (b) Translation of $\begin{pmatrix} 0 \\ -2 \end{pmatrix}$

3. **(a)**

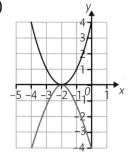

   (b)

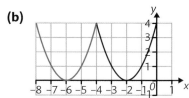

4. $(6, -2)$

Page 45 Algebraic fractions

Quick quiz:

(a) 12 **(b)** 60 **(c)** $x(x + 2)$ **(d)** $(x - 1)(x + 5)$

Questions:

1. $\dfrac{5x - 10}{6}$ 2. $\dfrac{9x + 7}{(x + 3)(x - 1)}$ 3. $\dfrac{41}{60x}$

4. $\dfrac{x + 5}{x - 6}$ 5. $\dfrac{3x - 4}{x - 1}$ 6. $n = \dfrac{2m}{3 - m}$

7. $x = \dfrac{3y - 4}{5 + y}$ 8. $\dfrac{2(x - 5)}{x^2(x - 6)}$ 9. $\dfrac{11x - 53}{x - 5}$

Page 46 Quadratics and fractions

Quick quiz:

(a) $x = -9$ and $x = -4$ **(b)** $x = 2.5$ and $x = -3$

Questions:

1. $x = 0$ and $x = -2$ 2. $x = \dfrac{1}{14}$

3. $x = 1$ and $x = \dfrac{1}{6}$ 4. $x = -1$ and $x = 6$

5. $x = 0.5$ and $x = 3$

Page 47 Function notation

Quick quiz:

1. **(a)** 11 **(b)** -10
2. **(a)** $x = 2$ **(b)** $x = -8$ and $x = -5$

Questions:

1. **(a) (i)** 3 **(ii)** 8
   (b) $x = 1$, $x = \dfrac{1}{5}$ **(c)** $x = -1$, $x = \dfrac{3}{5}$
2. **(a)** $12x + 11$ **(b)** $x = -3$
3. **(a)** 23 **(b)** $x = -\dfrac{1}{3}$ and $x = 1$
4. **(a)** $x = 1$, $x = -3$ **(b)** $x = \pm\sqrt{16.5}$

5. $ff(x) = \dfrac{1}{1 - \dfrac{1}{1 - x}} = \dfrac{1}{\dfrac{1(1 - x) - 1}{1 - x}} = \dfrac{1}{\dfrac{1 - x - 1}{1 - x}}$
   $= \dfrac{1 - x}{-x} = \dfrac{x - 1}{x}$

6. $x = 1$, $x = 8$

Page 48 Inverse functions

Quick quiz:

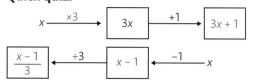

Questions:

1. $\dfrac{x - 5}{3}$

2. **(a)** $\dfrac{4x + 3}{x}$ **(b)** $x = 0.5$

3. **(a)** $\dfrac{x}{2x - 3}$ **(b)** $\dfrac{6x^2 + 9}{4x^2 + 5}$

4. **(a)** $x^2 - 3$ **(b)** $x + 3$
   (c) $x = -2$ and $x = 3$

5. **(a)** 1 **(b)** 29 **(c)** $\dfrac{x + 5}{2}$
   (d) $x = 4$ and $x = 1$

Page 49 Equation of a circle

Quick quiz:

$x^2 + y^2 = r^2$, radius

Questions:

1. 12
2. **(a)** $(-1)^2 + (-7)^2 = 1 + 49 = 50$
   (b) $r = \sqrt{50}$ or $5\sqrt{2}$

3. (a)

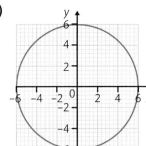

(b) approximately
$x = 3.7, y = 4.7$ or
$x = -4.7, y = -3.7$

4. $(-3.679, -0.679), (3.679, 0.679)$ **5.** $(-2, -4)$ and $\left(\dfrac{4}{5}, \dfrac{22}{5}\right)$

6. $y = \dfrac{4}{7}x + \dfrac{65}{7}$

Page 50 Iteration

Quick quiz:

(a) 1.79   **(b)** 0.41   **(c)** 3.62

Questions:

1. (a)

x	0	1	2	3	4	5
y	-10	-17	-18	-7	22	75

(b) From the table, the value changes sign between 3 and 4, so the solution lies between these values.

(c) $x^3 = 8x + 10$
$x = \sqrt[3]{8x + 10}$

(d) 3.32

2. (a) Substituting values 2 and 3 gives solutions of -4 and 9, which are 'either side' of -2, so the solution lies between 2 and 3.

(b) $x^3 = 6x - 2$
$x = \sqrt[3]{6x - 2}$

(c) 2.26

3. (a) $x(1 + x) = 3, x = \dfrac{3}{1 + x}$

(b) $x_1 = 1.5, x_2 = 1.2, x_3 = 1.3636$

Page 51 Exam skills: Algebra

Questions:

1. (a)

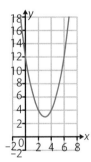

(b) Yes as the minimum point $(1, -1)$ is below the x–axis, so there are 2 real roots.

2. $a = -1, b = 2$

3. (a) £30 000

(b) The multiplier, 0.8, is less than 1.

(c) £9830.40

(d) 4 years

(e)

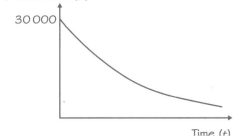

Page 52 Ratio

Quick quiz:

(a) 1:4   **(b)** 2:3   **(c)** 8:3   **(d)** 15:8

Questions:

1. 1.25 kg   **2.** 120 cm   **3.** 36%

4. (a) Cement weighs 200 kg, sand weighs 600 kg, gravel weighs 1400 kg

(b) No, as he needs 61 600 kg (61.6 tonnes).

Page 53 Proportion

Quick quiz:

(a) 48p   **(b)** £1.60

Questions:

1. Italy

2. Yes, as it will take 12.8 days.

3. 39

Page 54 Compound measures

Quick quiz:

1. two   **2.** speed, density

Questions:

1. 3.75 m²   **2.** 67 mins and 30 seconds

3. Carina

Page 55 Speed

Quick quiz:

1. 10 mph   **2.** 480 m   **3.** $6\frac{2}{3}$ hours

Questions:

1. 48 mph

2. No, she drives at an average speed of 46.7 mph.

3. No, as Tom arrives at 14:17.

4. Motorbike A = 170 mph   Motorbike B = 150 mph
Motorbike A is faster.

Page 56 Density

Quick quiz:

(a) density = mass ÷ volume

(b) mass = density × volume

(c) volume = mass ÷ density

Questions:

1. 5.2 kg/m³   **2.** 5.7 m³   **3.** 156.8 g

4. 11.6 g/cm³   **5.** 19.3 g/cm³   **6.** 11

Page 57 Proportion and graphs

Quick quiz:

(a) A   **(b)** C

Questions:

1. 67.2

2. No, Adam drove further.

3. (a) $a = \dfrac{2}{\sqrt{k}}, b = 2\sqrt{k}$ **(b)** $k = \frac{1}{3}$

Page 58 Proportionality formulae

Quick quiz:

y is inversely proportional to x.

Questions:

1. (a) $y = \dfrac{x}{36}$ **(b)** 20

2. 33.2

3. (a) 810   **(b)** 48

Page 59 Harder relationships

Quick quiz:

(a) a^2 **(b)** b^3 **(c)** $\sqrt{c}$ **(d)** $\sqrt[n]{d}$

Questions:

1. (a) $y = 0.75x^3$ **(b)** 8

2. (a) $P = \dfrac{250}{r^2}$ **(b)** 160   **(c)** 5

3. (a) $y = \dfrac{5}{6}\sqrt{x}$ **(b)** 81

4.

x	2	5	10	20
y	50	8	2	0.5

Page 60 Exam skills: Ratio and proportion

Questions:

1. $\dfrac{2}{3}$ **2. (a)** $y = \dfrac{16}{x^2}$ **(b)** $\dfrac{4}{5}$

(c)
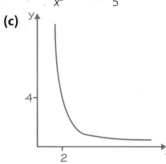

Page 61 Angle properties

Quick quiz:

(a) equal   **(b)** equal   **(c)** equal

(d) 180°   **(e)** 180°   **(f)** 360°

Questions:

1. Angle $CBD = 48°$ (Angles on a straight line add up to 180°)

    Angle $CDB = 104°$ (Angles in a triangle add up to 180°)

    $x = 104°$ (Corresponding angles)

2. Angle $CBE = 44°$ (Corresponding angles)

    $ABE = x = 180° - 44° = 136°$ (Angles on a straight line add up to 180°)

3. Angle $AED = 42°$ (Alternate angles)

    Angle $ADE = 69°$ (Base angles in an isosceles triangle are equal)

    $x = 111°$ (Angles on a straight line add up to 180°)

Page 62 Angle problems

Quick quiz:

(a) alternate   **(b)** corresponding

(c) vertically opposite

Questions:

1. Angle $DBC = 39°$ (Corresponding angles)

    $x = 108°$ (Angles in a triangle add up to 180°)

2. Angle $MRQ = x$ (Alternate angles)

    Angle $QMR = x$ (Base angles in an isosceles triangle are equal)

    $y = 180° - 2x$ (Angles in a triangle add up to 180°)

3. Angle $YWR = 51°$ (Angles on a straight line add up to 180°)

    $x = 51°$ (Alternate angles)

Page 63 Angles in polygons

Quick quiz:

1. (a) 360°   **(b)** 180°

2. (a) 60°   **(b)** 24

Questions:

1. 150°   **2.** 105°   **3.** 150°   **4.** 22.5°

Page 64 Constructing perpendiculars

Quick quiz:

(a) half   **(b)** 90°

Questions:

1.
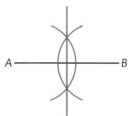

2.
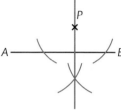

3.
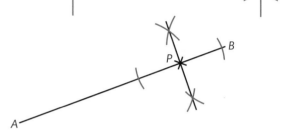

Page 65 Constructions, plans and elevations

Quick quiz:

(a) equilateral   **(b)** bisect, 90°   **(c)** bisect, 60°

Questions:

1.
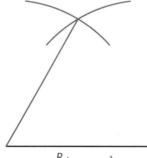

2.
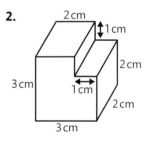

3.
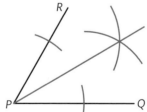

Page 66 Loci

Quick quiz:

(a) 30 km   **(b)** 400 m   **(c)** 2.5 cm

Questions:

1.
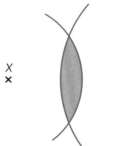

2. (a)

$A\times$ $\times B$

(b)

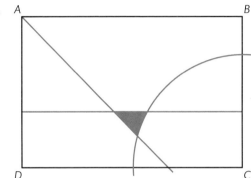

3.

P ——— Q

Page 67 Perimeter and area
Quick quiz:

(a) $l \times w$ **(b)** $0.5 \times b \times h$ **(c)** πr^2

Questions:

1. 24 cm
2. **(a)** $\pi(r + 1)^2 - \pi r^2 = \frac{1}{5}\pi r^2$; $r^2 - 10r - 5 = 0$
   (b) 345 m²
3. **(a)** $(x + 1)(2x - 3) + 2x(x + 2) = 50$
   or $(x - 1)(x + 2) + (x + 1)(3x - 1) = 50$
   $4x^2 + 3x - 53 = 0$
   (b) 3.28

Page 68 Volumes of 3D shapes
Quick quiz:

(a) $\frac{1}{3}\pi r^2 h$ **(b)** $\frac{4}{3}\pi r^3$ **(c)** $\frac{1}{3}a^2 h$

Questions:

1. 603 cm³   **2. (a)** 1026π cm³ **(b)** The volume will be larger
3. 8250 cm³

Page 69 Surface area
Quick quiz:

(a) $\pi r l + \pi r^2$ **(b)** $2\pi r^2 + 2\pi rh$ **(c)** $4\pi r^2$

Questions:

1. 252π cm²   **2.** 391 cm²   **3.** 707 cm²

Page 70 Prisms
Quick quiz:

(a) same   **(b)** cross-sectional area × length

Questions:

1. **(a)** 660 cm²   **(b)** 600 cm³
2. **(a)** 720 cm³   **(b)** 528.2 cm²
3. No, as 640 is less than 830.

Page 71 Circles and cylinders
Quick quiz:

1. **(a)** $2\pi r$ **(b)** πr^2 **(c)** $2\pi r^2 + 2\pi rh$ **(d)** $\pi r^2 h$
2. **(a)** 1100 cm³   **(b)** 597 cm²

Questions:

1. 9890 m²   **2.** 994   **3.** $15\sqrt{3} - 2\sqrt{5}$

Page 72 Circles, sectors and arcs
Quick quiz:

(a) $2\pi r \times \dfrac{\theta}{360}$ **(b)** $\pi r^2 \times \dfrac{\theta}{360}$

Questions:

1. **(a)** 6.11 cm   **(b)** 21.4 cm²
2. £22.68   **3.** 7.37 cm²
4. **(a)** 40.8 cm   **(b)** 86.4 cm²

Page 73 Circle facts
Quick quiz:

(a) straight   **(b)** perpendicular   **(c)** equal

Questions:

1. Angle $OTP = 90°$. Tangent meets radius at right angles.
   Angle $POT = 38°$. Angles in a triangle add up to 180°.
   Angle $ROT = 142°$. Angles on a straight line add up to 180°.
   Angle $TRO = 19°$. Base angles in an isosceles triangle are equal.
2. Angle OBC = Angle $OAC = 90°$. Tangent meets radius at right angles.
   Angle $AOB = 132°$. Angles in a quadrilateral add up to 360°.
   Angle $OBA = 24°$. Base angles in an isosceles triangle are equal.
3. Angle $ABT = 76°$. Angles in a triangle add up to 180°.
   Angle OAB = Angle $OBA = 29°$. Tangent meets radius at right angles, and base angles in an isosceles triangle are equal.
   Angle $OBT = 76 + 29 = 105°$

Page 74 Circle theorems
Quick quiz:

(a) twice   **(b)** equal   **(c)** 90°   **(d)** 180°

Questions:

1. **(a)** Angle $ABD = 90°$ (Angle subtended by diameter at circumference is 90°)
   Angle $ADB = 36°$ (Angles in a triangle add up to 180°)
   (b) Angle $BCD = 126°$ (Opposite angles in a cyclic quadrilateral add up to 180°)
2. Angle $BOA = 158°$ (Angle subtended at the centre is twice the angle subtended at the circumference)
   Angle $APB = 22°$ (Angles in a quadrilateral add up to 360°)
3. Angle $BDP = 78°$ (Alternate segment theorem)
   Angle $ADP = 78 - 26 = 52°$

Page 75 Transformations
Quick quiz:

reflection, rotation, translation, enlargement

Questions:

1.

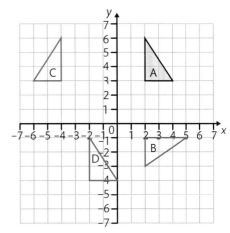

2. (a) Rotation 90° anticlockwise about (−1, −2)

(b) Reflection in $y = -x$

(c) Translation of $\begin{pmatrix} 2 \\ -3 \end{pmatrix}$

3. C

Page 76 Enlargement

Quick quiz:

(a) larger   **(b)** smaller   **(c)** opposite

Questions:

1.

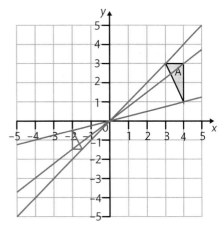

2. Enlargement about (1, 3) of scale factor 2

3.

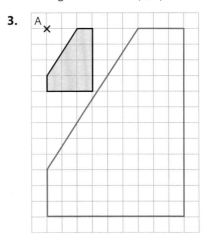

Page 77 Combining transformations

Quick quiz:

(a) congruent   **(b)** congruent

(c) congruent   **(d)** similar

1. Rotation of 180° about (0, −1)

2. Reflection in the line $x = 0$

3. Rotation 90° clockwise about (−3, 1)

Page 78 Bearings

Quick quiz:

(a) north, three   **(b)** A   **(c)** B

Questions:

1. (a) 044°   **(b)** 112°   **(c)** 078°

2. 233°

3. 138°

Page 79 Scale drawings and maps

Quick quiz:

(a) 90 km   **(b)** 3.25 cm

Questions:

1. (a) 040°   **(b)** 66 km

2. (a) 73 km   **(b)** 100°

(c)

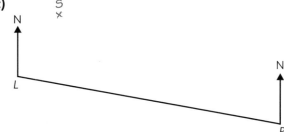

Page 80 Similar shapes

Quick quiz:

(a) $\dfrac{8}{5}$ **(b)** $\dfrac{5}{3}$ **(c)** $\dfrac{25}{16}$ **(d)** $\dfrac{27}{8}$

Questions:

1. (a) 180 cm²   **(b)** 120 cm³

2. 192 cm²

3. (a) 640 cm³   **(b)** 40 cm²

4. 102.4 cm³

Page 81 Congruent triangles

Quick quiz:

SSS

Questions:

1. Angle $ACB = 65°$. Angle $DFE = 80°$. Side AB = side $EF = 5$ cm, so the triangles are congruent (ASA).

2. $BC = CD$ because the shape is a rhombus. $DM = BM$ because M is the midpoint of DB.

The two triangles share side MC. They are congruent (SSS).

3. $AB = AD$, $BC = DC$, both triangles contain AC, so the triangles are congruent (SSS).

Page 82 Pythagoras' theorem

Quick quiz:

1. $a^2 + b^2 = c^2$

2. (a) $\sqrt{45}$ cm   **(b)** $\sqrt{51}$ cm   **(c)** $\sqrt{55}$ cm

Questions:

1. 86.5 cm   2. 2.19 kg   3. 18.7 cm²

Page 83 Pythagoras' theorem in 3D

Quick quiz:

(a) $\sqrt{136}$ cm or 11.7 cm   (b) $\sqrt{176}$ cm or 13.3 cm

Questions:

1. 17.6 cm   2. 84.1 cm

3. Yes, as the wooden frame costs £54.11.

Page 84 Units of length, area and volume

Quick quiz:

(a) 10 mm   (b) 100 cm   (c) 1000 mm   (d) 1000 m

Questions:

1. (a) 0.48 cm²   (b) 45.2 m²

2. 192   3. 227 km   4. 86.1 cm

Page 85 Trigonometry: lengths

Quick quiz:

(a) $\dfrac{\text{opp}}{\text{hyp}}$ (b) $\dfrac{\text{adj}}{\text{hyp}}$ (c) $\dfrac{\text{opp}}{\text{adj}}$

Questions:

1. 47.6

2. (a) 5.32 cm (b) 9.61 cm   3. 11.9 cm

4. Donna has substituted AB and 12 incorrectly, the opposite is 12 and the hypotenuse is AB. Donna has rounded her final answer to 4 significant figures, not 3. The correct answer should be 18.7 m.

Page 86 Trigonometry: angles

Quick quiz:

(a) 73.8°   (b) 51.3°   (c) 70.1°

Questions:

1. $\dfrac{\sqrt{3}}{2}$

2. 34.2°   3. 45.1°   4. 30.3°

Page 87 Trigonometry techniques

Quick quiz:

(a) $\sqrt{3}$ (b) $\dfrac{1}{\sqrt{2}}$ (c) $\dfrac{\sqrt{3}}{2}$

Questions:

1. (a) 30°   (b) 60°   (c) 45°

2. No, angle is 60°.

3. 60 m

Page 88 Trigonometry in 3D

Quick quiz:

(a) 16.8   (b) 56.8   (c) 30.2

Questions:

1. (a) 19.7 cm   (b) 24.0°

2. 35.3°   3. 55.9°

Page 89 The sine rule

Quick quiz:

(a) $\dfrac{a}{\sin A} = \dfrac{b}{\sin B} = \dfrac{c}{\sin C}$ (b) $\dfrac{\sin A}{a} = \dfrac{\sin B}{b} = \dfrac{\sin C}{c}$

Questions:

1. (a) 41.4°   (b) 5.11 cm   2. 23.1 cm

3. 5.28 km

Page 90 The cosine rule

Quick quiz:

(a) $a^2 = b^2 + c^2 - 2bc \cos A$ (b) $\cos A = \dfrac{b^2 + c^2 - a^2}{2bc}$

Questions:

1. 24.7 cm   2. 105°   3. $x = \dfrac{2}{3}$

Page 91 Triangles and segments

Quick quiz:

(a) 18.2 cm²   (b) 7.85 cm   (c) 58.9 cm²

Questions:

1. 156 cm²   2. 130 cm   3. 203 cm²

Page 92 Vectors

Quick quiz:

(a) direction, magnitude

(b) column, movement in x-direction, movement in y-direction

Questions:

1. $\begin{pmatrix} 4 \\ 7 \end{pmatrix}$ 2. $\begin{pmatrix} -6 \\ 4 \end{pmatrix}$

3. (a) 5**b**   (b) **a** + **b**   (c) 4**b** − **a**

4. (a) 2**a**   (b) 2**a** + **b**   (c) **b** − **a**

Page 93 Vector proof

Quick quiz:

(a) direction, magnitude   (b) direction

Questions:

1. $k = \dfrac{1}{3}$ so $\overrightarrow{AD} = \dfrac{1}{3}(5\mathbf{a} + 7\mathbf{b})$

2. $\overrightarrow{EF} = \dfrac{\mathbf{a} + \mathbf{b}}{2}$, $\overrightarrow{EC} = 2(\mathbf{a} + \mathbf{b})$ hence $\overrightarrow{EC} = 4\overrightarrow{EF}$

3. $\overrightarrow{BC} = -7\mathbf{a} + 3\mathbf{b}$
   $\overrightarrow{BD} = \dfrac{3}{5}\overrightarrow{BC}$
   $\overrightarrow{AD} = \overrightarrow{AB} + \overrightarrow{BD} = \dfrac{1}{5}(14\mathbf{a} + 9\mathbf{b})$

Page 94 Line segments

Quick quiz:

(a) Pythagoras'   (b) $\left(\dfrac{x_1 + x_2}{2}, \dfrac{y_1 + y_2}{2} \right)$

Questions:

1. (a) (−1, 2.5)   (b) $3\sqrt{5}$

2. (a) (9, 7)   (b) $2\sqrt{13}$

3. (a) (−0.5, 3.5)   (b) 8.60

Page 95 Exam skills: Geometry and measures

Questions:

1. Yes as $2\begin{pmatrix} -4 \\ -1 \end{pmatrix} + 3\begin{pmatrix} 3 \\ -1 \end{pmatrix} = \begin{pmatrix} 2 \times -4 \\ 2 \times -1 \end{pmatrix} + \begin{pmatrix} 3 \times 3 \\ 3 \times -1 \end{pmatrix}$
   $= \begin{pmatrix} -8 + 9 \\ -2 - 3 \end{pmatrix} = \begin{pmatrix} 1 \\ -5 \end{pmatrix}$.

2. 19.4 cm   3. 27.1°

Page 96 Probability

Quick quiz:

(a) $\frac{1}{2}$ **(b)** $\frac{2}{3}$ **(c)** $\frac{1}{6}$

Questions:

1. **(a)** 0.15 **(b)** 0.1064
2. **(a)** 0.001 **(b)** 0.027
3. **(a)** $\frac{1}{36}$ **(b) (i)** $\frac{5}{36}$ **(ii)** $\frac{125}{216}$

Page 97 Relative frequency

Quick quiz:

$\frac{2}{5}$

Questions:

1. **(a)** $\frac{2}{15}$ **(b)** $\frac{4}{5}$ **(c)** $\frac{13}{30}$
2. **(a)** $\frac{1}{2}$ **(b)** $\frac{7}{8}$ **(c)** $\frac{7}{200}$
3. **(a)** Sarah has the more reliable results as she rolls the dice more times.

   (b) $\frac{455}{5184}$

Page 98 Venn diagrams

Quick quiz:

outcomes that can occur together.

Questions:

1. **(a)**

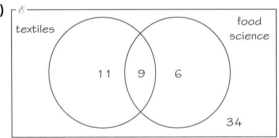

   (b) $\frac{17}{30}$ **(c)** $\frac{17}{60}$

2. **(a)**

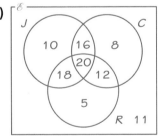

   (b) (i) $\frac{11}{100}$ **(ii)** $\frac{23}{100}$
3. **(a)** A' ∩ B **(b)** A' ∪ B'

Page 99 Conditional probability

Quick quiz:

has

Questions:

1. **(a) (i)** $\frac{19}{50}$ **(ii)** $\frac{1}{5}$ **(b)** $\frac{4}{19}$
2. **(a)** $\frac{11}{60}$ **(b)** $\frac{11}{27}$ 3. $\frac{103}{150}$

Page 100 Tree diagrams

Quick quiz:

tree diagram

Questions:

1. **(a)**

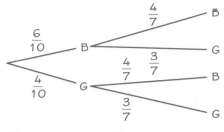

   (b) $\frac{12}{35}$ **(c)** $\frac{17}{35}$

2. **(a)**

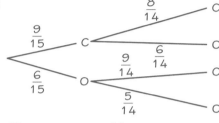

   (b) $\frac{12}{35}$ **(c)** $\frac{18}{35}$

3. **(a)**

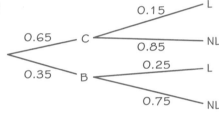

   (b) $\frac{39}{400}$

Page 101 Exam skills: Probability

Questions:

1. **(a)** $\frac{48}{121}$ **(b)** $\frac{24}{55}$

2. **(a)**

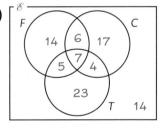

   (b) $\frac{3}{5}$ **(c)** $\frac{4}{13}$

Page 102 Sampling

Quick quiz:

all the individuals in the population have an equal chance of being chosen

Questions:

1. **(a)**

	Thriller	Horror	Science fiction	Musical
Tally				
Frequency				

   (b) He is only asking people in his office. The sample too small.

2. Number each bolt.

Use random numbers to select the bolts.

3. He is only asking his friends at school. The sample is too small and it is biased.

4. Only asking men at the railway station so the results are likely to be biased. A sample of 10 is too small.

Page 103 Mean, median and mode
Quick quiz:

1. (**a**) most frequent

(**b**) middle number of an ordered set of numbers

(**c**) add up all the values and divide by the number of values

2. 1470 cm

Questions:

1. 106

2. 14, 14, 17, 19, 26

3. 16 s

4. 10.6 °C

Page 104 Frequency tables
Quick quiz:

(**a**) 5

(**b**) 8

(**c**) 8.4

Questions:

1. (**a**) 0

(**b**) 1

(**c**) 1.29

2. (**a**) $20 \leqslant t < 30$

(**b**) 27.8 minutes

(**c**) The data is grouped.

Page 105 Interquartile range
Quick quiz:

7

Questions:

1. 27

2. 6.6 kg, 23.0 kg

3. (**a**)

```
4 | 8
5 | 2 4 5 5
6 | 0 1 4 4 5 6 8 8
7 | 2 8
```

(**b**) 30

(**c**) 13

Key 4 | 8 represents 48

Page 106 Line graphs
Quick quiz:

(**a**) 36

(**b**) 18

(**c**) 20.9

Questions:

1. (**a**)

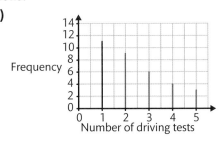

(**b**) 1

(**c**) 2.36

2. (**a**) 162

(**b**) downwards

Page 107 Scatter graphs
Quick quiz:

(**a**) positive

(**b**) negative

Questions:

1. (**a**) (140, 60)

(**b**) (**i**) suitable line of best fit   (**ii**) positive   (**c**) 63 kg

(**d**) No, as 180 cm is out of the data range/extrapolation

2. (**a**)

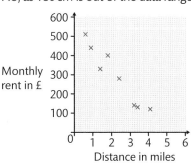

(**b**) Negative; as the distance from the city centre increases, the rent decreases.

(**c**) £230

(**d**) Yes, as 2.8 miles is within the data range.

Page 108 Cumulative frequency
Quick quiz:

Grouped data from a frequency table

Questions:

1. (**a**)

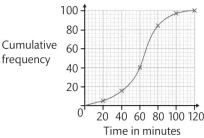

(**b**) 64 minutes

(**c**) 29 minutes

(**d**) 8

2. (**a**)

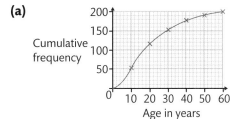

(**b**) 20 years

(**c**) 15%

Page 109 Box plots
Quick quiz:

21

Questions:

1. (**a**)

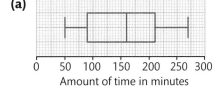

(**b**) Median of the boys is greater than the median of the girls.

IQR/range of the boys is greater than the IQR/range of the girls.

The boys on average spend more time playing in the garden than the girls.

The boys' times are more spread out than the girls' times.

2. (a)

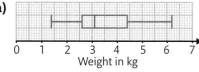

Weight in kg

(b) 60

Page 110 Histograms

Quick quiz:

$$\text{frequency density} = \frac{\text{frequency}}{\text{class width}}$$

Questions:

1. (a)

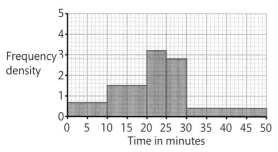

(b) 30 or 31

2. $\dfrac{16}{25}$

Page 111 Frequency polygons

Quick quiz:

(a) 10 **(b)** 17.5 **(c)** 24 **(d)** 35

Questions:

1. (a)

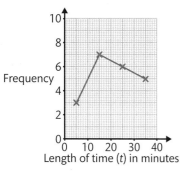

Length of time (t) in minutes

(b) $10 < t \leqslant 20$ **(c)** $20 < t \leqslant 30$

2. (a)

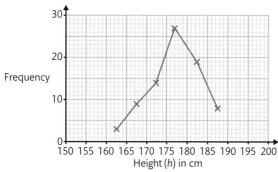

Height (h) in cm

(b) $\dfrac{27}{40}$

Page 112 Analysing data

Quick quiz:

Boys on average take longer to walk home than girls.

Questions:

1.

	Male	Female
Median	72	76
IQR	12	11

Females on average take longer than males.

The spread of the times is about the same.

2.

	Median	IQR	Range
Amrit	33	8	11
Rob	34	13	18

Amrit is more consistent as his IQR/range is less than Rob's.

3. S1 : True, because age increases as the 31st person is more than 36 years old.

S2 : False, because the age of the 16th person in age order will not be less than 32.

Page 113 Exam skills: Statistics

Questions:

1. (a) 50 **(b)** $\dfrac{3}{10}$

2. (a)

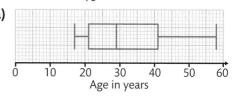

Age in years

(b) Median of the women is greater than the median of the men.

IQR/range of the men is greater than the IQR/range of the women.

The women are on average older than the men.

The ages of these men are more spread out than the ages of these women.

Page 114 Problem solving strategies

$AC = 8.7\,\text{m}$ $BC = 6.9\,\text{m}$ Perimeter $= 22.8\,\text{m}$

Cost of fence $=$ £222.30

£222.30 is less than £235, so Macey has enough money.

Page 115 Solving number problems

1. No, as the cost is £233.17. **2.** Bank A

Page 116 Solving proof problems

Questions

1. $n^2 - 2n + 1 + n^2 + n^2 + 2n + 1 = 3n^2 + 2$

2. $n^2 + 8n + 16 - 3n - 4 = n^2 + 5n + 12$
$= n^2 + 5n + 4 + 8 = (n + 1)(n + 4) + 8$

3. $n^2 + 2 - n^2 + 4n - 4 = 4n - 2 = 2(2n - 1)$

4. $9n^2 + 6n + 1 - (9n^2 - 6n + 1) = 12n = 6(2n)$

5. Consecutive odd numbers are $2n + 1$ and $2n + 3$
$(2n + 3)^2 - (2n + 1)^2 = 4n^2 + 12n + 9 - 4n^2 - 4n - 1$
$= 8n + 8 = 8(n + 1)$

6. Consecutive even numbers are $2n, 2n + 2$ and $2n + 4$.
$(2n)^2 + (2n + 2)^2 + (2n + 4)^2$
$= 4n^2 + 4n^2 + 8n + 4 + 4n^2 + 16n + 16$
$= 12n^2 + 24n + 20 = 4(3n^2 + 6n + 5)$

Page 117 Solving geometric problems

1. $AC^2 = x^2 + x^2 - (2 \times x \times x \times \cos 45) = x^2(2 - \sqrt{2})$
$DE^2 = 5^2 + 5^2 - (2 \times 5 \times 5 \times \cos\theta) = 50 - 50\cos\theta$
$AC = DE$ so $50 - 50\cos\theta = x^2(2 - \sqrt{2})$

$$\cos\theta = 1 - \frac{(2 - \sqrt{2})}{50}x^2$$

2. $\overrightarrow{EC} = 2\mathbf{a} - 2\mathbf{b}$

$\overrightarrow{DB} = \mathbf{a} - 3\mathbf{b}$ so $\overrightarrow{DF} = \dfrac{1}{2}(\mathbf{a} - 3\mathbf{b})$

$\overrightarrow{EF} = \mathbf{b} + \dfrac{1}{2}(\mathbf{a} - 3\mathbf{b}) = \dfrac{1}{2}(\mathbf{a} - \mathbf{b})$

$\overrightarrow{EC}$ is a multiple of $\overrightarrow{EF}$ so the lines are parallel. Also, as E is on both lines, EFC is a single straight line.

Page 118 Solving algebraic problems

1. $8\,\text{cm}^3$

2. (a) $46 = 2x + 2\sqrt{17^2 - x^2}$

$23 = x + \sqrt{17^2 - x^2}$

$(23 - x)^2 = 17^2 - x^2$

$23^2 - 46x + x^2 = 17^2 - x^2$

$2x^2 - 46x + 240 = 0$

$x^2 - 23x + 120 = 0$

(b) $120\,\text{cm}^2$

Page 119 Solving statistical problems

1. £660

2. (a)

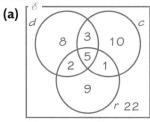

(b) $\dfrac{11}{30}$ **(c)** $\dfrac{7}{18}$

Page 120 Non-calculator practice paper

1. $2^4 \times 3$

2. $5n + 1$

3. $60\,\text{km/h}$

4. (a) 43 minutes

(b) The table does not show the exact data values so the mean is an estimate.

5. Ariana = 12, Samir = 24, Carla = 20

6. Angle $ABD = 32°$ because base angles in an isosceles triangle are equal.

Angle $BDC = 32°$ because alternate angles are equal.
$x = 74°$ because base angles in an isosceles triangle are equal and angles in a triangle sum to 180°.

7. $16 - 4\pi$

8. $x = 0.51818181818$

$10x = 5.1818181818$

$1000x = 518.18181818$

Subtracting: $990x = 513$

$x = \dfrac{513}{990} = \dfrac{57}{110}$

9. The points are not plotted at the midpoints of the class intervals.

10. $x = 2$

11. Yes, $7.3 \times 10^{-5} \times 1000 = 7.3 \times 10^{-2} = 0.073$

12. (a) 9   **(b)** 16

13. adult = £4.50; child = £3.25

14. (a)

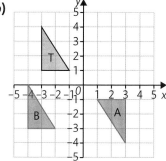

(b) The interquartile range is greater for the men.

15. (a) 245   **(b)** $x < 340$

16. $\dfrac{a + b}{b - 2a} = \dfrac{t}{3}$

$3(a + b) = t(b - 2a)$

$3a + 3b = bt - 2at$

$3a + 2at = bt - 3b$

$a(3 + 2t) = b(t - 3)$

$a = \dfrac{b(t - 3)}{3 + 2t}$

17. $y = 22x^3$

18. $(n + 2)^2 + n^2 + (n - 2)^2 = n^2 + 4n + 4 + n^2 + n^2 - 4n + 4$
$= 3n^2 + 8$

19. No, because it can be a reflection in $x = 0$.

20. $y = 3x - 10$

21. $a = 2$ and $b = 1$ $y = \sqrt{3} + 1$

22. $a = 1$ and $b = -1$

23. $x > 8$

24. (a) $a = 2$ and $b = -5$ **(b)** (i) $(2, -1)$ (ii) $(2, 5)$

Page 123 Calculator practice paper

1. $x = 3$ **2.** $25x^6y^4$ **3.** 7×10^8 **4.** $(4, 5)$

5. 93.8%   **6. (a)** $1.11\,\text{g/cm}^3$ **(b)** The calculated estimate of the density will decrease.

7. $\dfrac{1}{19}$ **8. (a) and (b)**

(c) $(-2, 0)$

9. (a) $x = 7$ **(b)** $y = 3$

10. 2.309180552

11. 28.4°

12. Penn pumps = 69.4 hours

Wulfrun pumps = 100 hours

They should use Penn pumps.

13. (a) 1.36

(b) The truck is travelling at 1.36 km/min or 81.6 km/h

14.

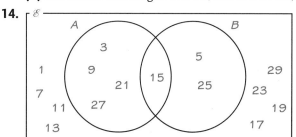

15. 12° **16.** 57.1 cm²

17. (a) £92 200 **(b)** 11.6%

18.

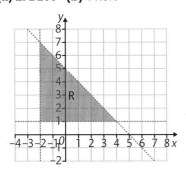

19. (a)

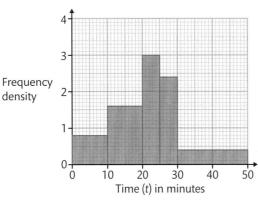

(b) $\frac{29}{59}$

20. No, he is not correct as 195 ÷ 12 is not a whole number.

21. On square-rooting both sides, he has forgotten to include the negative square root. He hasn't rationalis⸱ the denominator.

22. Gradient of AC $-\frac{1}{2}$, gradient of MN $-\frac{1}{2}$, so MN is parallel to AC.

23. $\frac{7}{25}$

24. Point of intersection = (2, −6)

There is only one point of intersection, so the line is ⸱ tangent to the circle.

25. (a) 4

(b) $2n - 2$

(c) 99 would not be a term in this sequence, because all the terms in the sequence will be even numbe⸱

Published by BBC Active, an imprint of Educational Publishers LLP, part of the Pearson Education Group, 80 Strand, London, WC2R 0RL.

www.pearsonschools.co.uk/BBCBitesize

© Educational Publishers LLP 2018

BBC logo © BBC 1996. BBC and BBC Active are trademarks of the British Broadcasting Corporation.

Edited, typeset and produced by Elektra Media Ltd
Illustrated by Elektra Media Ltd
Cover design by Andrew Magee & Pearson Education Limited 2018
Cover illustration by Darren Lingard / Oxford Designers & Illustrators

The right of Navtej Marwaha to be identified as author of this work has been asserted by him in accordance with the Copyright, Designs and Patents Act 1988.

First published 2018

21 20 19 18
10 9 8 7 6 5 4 3 2 1

British Library Cataloguing in Publication Data

A catalogue record for this book is available from the British Library

ISBN 978 1 406 68606 7

Printed and bound in Slovakia by Neografia.

The Publisher's policy is to use paper manufactured from sustainable forests.

Note from the publisher

Pearson has robust editorial processes, including answer and fact checks, to ensure the accuracy of the content in this publication, and every effort is made to ensure this publication is free of errors. We are, however, only humar and occasionally errors do occur. Pearson is not liable for any misunderstandings that arise as a result of errors in th⸱ publication, but it is our priority to ensure that the conter is accurate. If you spot an error, please do contact us at resourcescorrections@pearson.com so we can make sure is corrected.

Websites

Pearson Education Limited is not responsible for the content of third-party websites.